Best in Children's Books

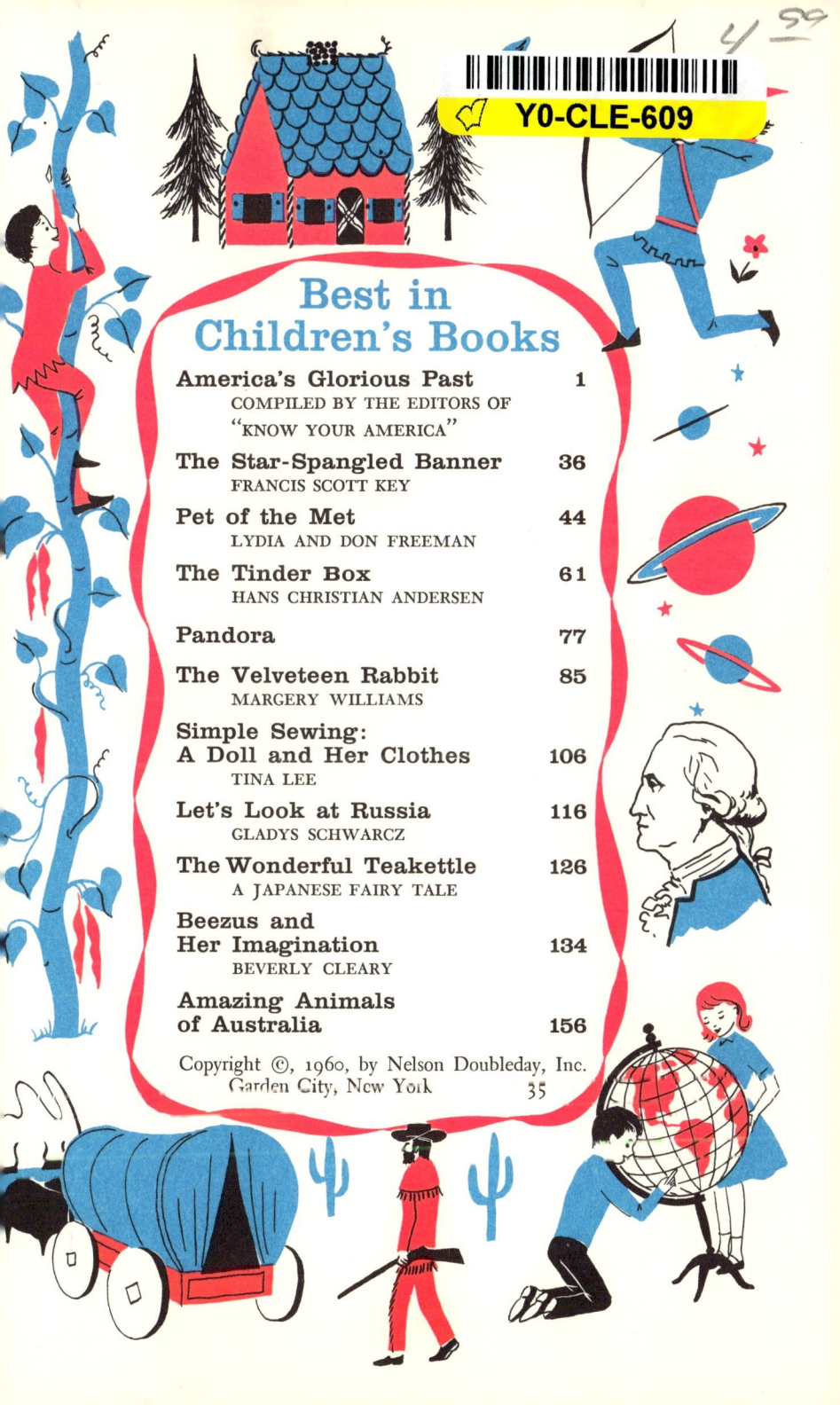

America's Glorious Past COMPILED BY THE EDITORS OF "KNOW YOUR AMERICA"	1
The Star-Spangled Banner FRANCIS SCOTT KEY	36
Pet of the Met LYDIA AND DON FREEMAN	44
The Tinder Box HANS CHRISTIAN ANDERSEN	61
Pandora	77
The Velveteen Rabbit MARGERY WILLIAMS	85
Simple Sewing: **A Doll and Her Clothes** TINA LEE	106
Let's Look at Russia GLADYS SCHWARCZ	116
The Wonderful Teakettle A JAPANESE FAIRY TALE	126
Beezus and **Her Imagination** BEVERLY CLEARY	134
Amazing Animals **of Australia**	156

Copyright ©, 1960, by Nelson Doubleday, Inc.
Garden City, New York

America's Glorious Past

compiled by the editors of "KNOW YOUR AMERICA"

paintings by ALICE SMITH

drawings by EDWARD SHENTON

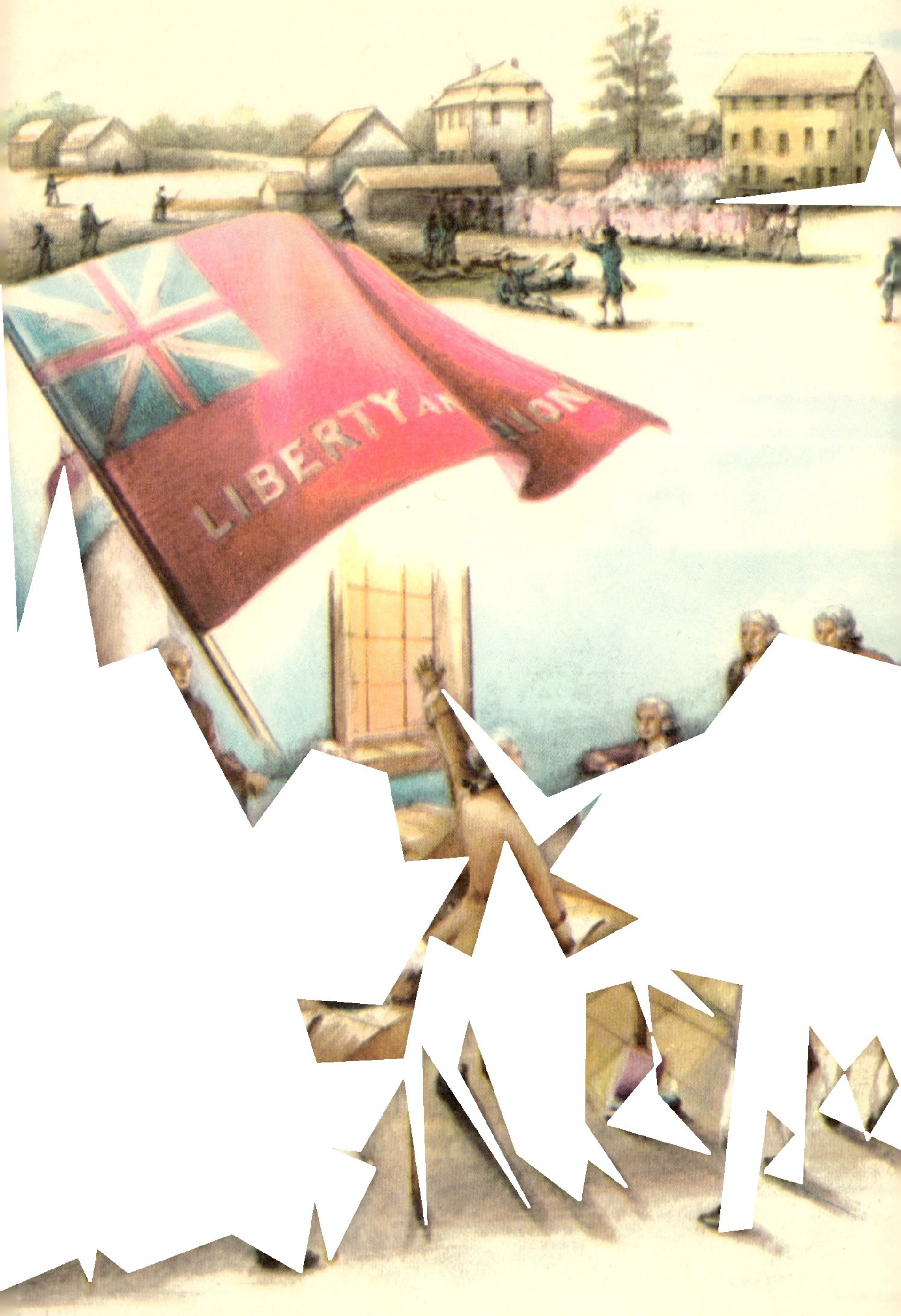
LIBERTY

GIVE ME LIBERTY, OR GIVE ME DEATH!

from Patrick Henry's THE CALL TO ARMS, *second Revolutionary Convention, at Richmond, Virginia, March 23, 1775*

There is a just God who presides over the destinies of nations; and who will raise up friends to fight our battles for us. The battle, sir, is not to the strong alone; it is to the vigilant, the active, the brave . . . There is no retreat but in submission and slavery! Our chains are forged! Their clanking may be heard on the plains of Boston! The war is inevitable—and let it come! I repeat it, sir, let it come! . . . Is life so dear, or peace so sweet, as to be purchased at the price of chains and slavery? Forbid it, Almighty God! I know not what course others may take; but as for me, give me liberty, or give me death!

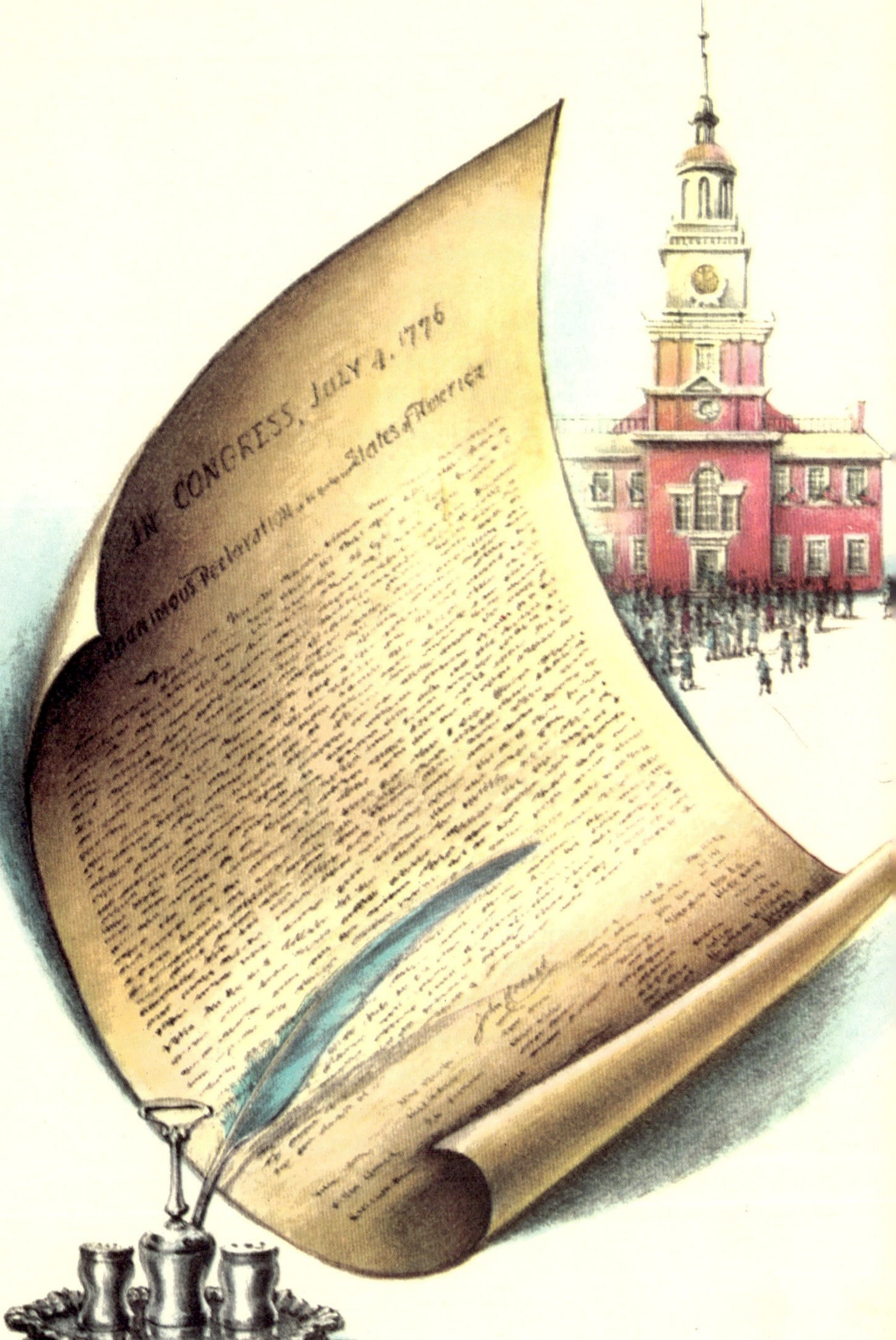
IN CONGRESS, JULY 4. 1776
States of America

LIFE, LIBERTY, AND THE PURSUIT OF HAPPINESS

from the DECLARATION OF INDEPENDENCE, *written by Thomas Jefferson, adopted by the Second Continental Congress, at Philadelphia, July 4, 1776*

WHEN in the Course of human events, it becomes necessary for one people to dissolve the political bands which have connected them with another, and to assume among the powers of the earth, the separate and equal station to which the Laws of Nature and of Nature's God entitle them, a decent respect to the opinions of mankind requires that they should declare the causes which impel them to the separation.

We hold these truths to be self-evident, that all men are created equal, that they are endowed by their Creator with certain unalienable Rights, that among these are Life, Liberty, and the pursuit of Happiness——That to secure these rights, Governments are instituted among Men, deriving their just powers from the consent of the governed, That whenever any form of government becomes destructive of these ends, it is the Right of the People to alter or to abolish it, and to institute new Government, laying its foundation on such principles and organizing its powers in such form, as to them shall seem most likely to effect their Safety and Happiness . . .

YANKEE DOODLE

> *sung by Continental troops as a marching song, 1775–1783*

*Yankee Doodle came to town,
 Riding on a pony;
He stuck a feather in his cap
 And called it macaroni.*

CHORUS

Yankee Doodle, keep it up,
 Yankee Doodle dandy,
Mind the music and the step,
 And with the girls be handy.

Father and I went down to camp,
 Along with Captain Goodin'
And there we saw the men and boys,
 As thick as hasty puddin'.

There was Captain Washington
 Upon a slapping stallion,
A-giving orders to his men—
 I guess there was a million.

And there I see a swamping gun,
 Large as a log of maple,
Upon a deuced little cart,
 A load for Father's cattle.

And every time they shoot it off,
   It takes a horn of powder,
And makes a noise like Father's gun,
   Only a nation louder.

It scared me so I hoofed it off,
   Nor stopped, as I remember,
Nor turned about till I got home,
   Locked up in Mother's chamber.

AMERICA

by the Reverend Samuel French Smith, and first publicly sung at the Park Street Church, Boston, on July 4, 1832

My country 'tis of thee,
Sweet land of liberty,
   Of thee I sing;
Land where my fathers died,
Land of the Pilgrims' pride,
From every mountainside
   Let Freedom ring.

My native country, thee,
Land of the noble free—
　　Thy name I love;
I love thy rocks and rills,
Thy woods and templed hills:
My heart with rapture thrills
　　Like that above.

Let music swell the breeze,
And ring from all the trees
　　Sweet Freedom's song;
Let mortal tongues awake,
Let all that breathe partake,
Let rocks their silence break—
　　The sound prolong.

Our fathers' God, to Thee,
Author of Liberty,
　　To Thee we sing:
Long may our land be bright
With Freedom's holy light;
Protect us by Thy might,
　　Great God, our King.

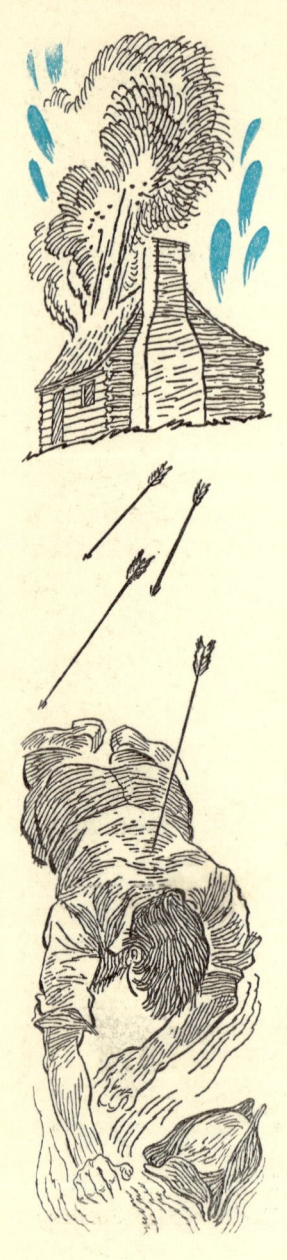

SONG OF THE SETTLERS

by JESSAMYN WEST

Freedom is a hard-bought thing—
A gift no man can give,
For some, a way of dying,
For most, a way to live.

Freedom is a hard-bought thing—
A rifle in the hand,
The horses hitched at sunup,
A harvest in the land.

Freedom is a hard-bought thing—
A massacre, a bloody rout,
The candles lit at nightfall,
And the night shut out.

Freedom is a hard-bought thing—
An arrow in the back,
The wind in the long corn rows,
And the hay in the rack.

Freedom is a way of living,
A song, a mighty cry.
Freedom is the bread we eat;
Let it be the way we die!

Text from *A Mirror for the Sky*, copyright, 1946, 1948, by Jessamyn West. Reprinted by permission of Harcourt, Brace and Company, Inc.

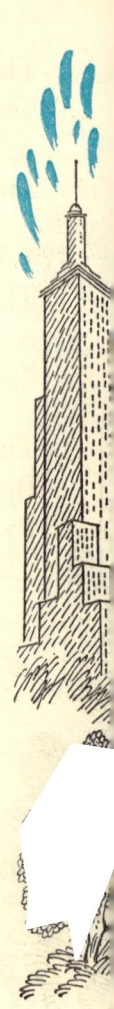

THE WILDERNESS IS TAMED

by ELIZABETH J. COATSWORTH

The axe has cut the forest down,
The laboring ox has smoothed all clear,
Apples now grow where pine trees stood,
And slow cows graze instead of deer.

Where Indian fires once raised their smoke
The chimneys of a farmhouse stand,
And cocks crow barnyard challenges
To dawns that once saw savage land.

The axe, the plow, the binding wall,
By these the wilderness is tamed,
By these the white man's will is wrought,
The rivers bridged, the new towns named.

Text from *Away Goes Sally*, copyright, 1934, by The Macmillan Company.

DIXIE

by Daniel Decatur Emmett. Written as a minstrel-show tune in 1859, DIXIE *became the rallying and marching song of the Southern states when they seceded from the Union in 1861.*

I wish I was in de land ob cotton,
Old times dar am not forgotten;
   Look away, look away, look away, Dixie land!
In Dixie land whar I was born in,
Early on one frosty mornin',
   Look away, look away, look away, Dixie land!

CHORUS

Den I wish I was in Dixie! Hooray! Hooray!
In Dixie's land we'll take our stand,
   to lib an' die in Dixie,
Away, away, away down south in Dixie!
Away, away, away down south in Dixie!

Dar's buckwheat cakes and Injun batter,
Makes you fat er a little fatter;
   Look away, look away, look away, Dixie land!
Den hoe it down an' scratch your grabbel,
To Dixie's land I'm bound to trabbel;
   Look away, look away, look away, Dixie land!

BATTLE-HYMN OF THE REPUBLIC

by Julia Ward Howe. The words were written in 1862, to be sung to the tune of JOHN BROWN'S BODY—*a favorite marching song of the Union troops.*

Mine eyes have seen the glory of the coming of the Lord;
He is trampling out the vintage where the grapes of wrath are stored;
He hath loosed the fateful lightning of His terrible swift sword;
    His truth is marching on.

I have seen Him in the watch-fires of a hundred circling camps;
They have builded Him an altar in the evening dews and damps;
I can read His righteous sentence by the dim and flaring lamps;
    His day is marching on.

I have read a fiery gospel, writ in burnished rows of steel:
"As ye deal with my contemners, so with you my grace shall deal;
Let the Hero, born of woman, crush the serpent with his heel,
    Since God is marching on."

He has sounded forth the trumpet that shall never call retreat;

He is sifting out the hearts of men before His judgment-
    seat:
Oh, be swift, my soul, to answer Him! be jubilant my feet!
    Our God is marching on.

In the beauty of the lilies Christ was born across the sea,
With a glory in His bosom that transfigures you and me;
As He died to make men holy, let us die to make men free,
    While God is marching on.

GOVERNMENT OF THE PEOPLE,
BY THE PEOPLE,
AND FOR THE PEOPLE . . .

THE GETTYSBURG ADDRESS, *delivered by President Abraham Lincoln, at a dedication ceremony on the battlefield at Gettysburg, on November 19, 1863*

Fourscore and seven years ago our fathers brought forth on this continent a new nation conceived in liberty and dedicated to the proposition that all men are created equal. Now we are engaged in a great civil war testing whether that nation, or any nation so conceived and so dedicated, can long endure. We are met on a great battlefield of that war. We have come to dedicate a portion of that field as a final resting place for those who here gave their lives that that nation might live. It is altogether fitting and proper that we should do this. But, in a larger sense, we cannot dedicate, we cannot consecrate, we cannot hallow this ground. The brave men, living and dead, who struggled here have consecrated it far above our poor power to add or detract. The world will little note nor long remember what we say here, but it can never forget what they did here. It is for us the living rather to be dedicated here to the unfinished work which they who fought here have thus far so nobly advanced. It is rather for us to be here dedicated to the great task remaining before us—that from these honoured dead we take increased devotion to that cause for which they gave the last full measure of devotion—that we here highly resolve that these dead shall not have died in vain, that this nation under God shall have a new birth of freedom, and that government of the people, by the people, and for the people, shall not perish from the earth.

A JUST AND LASTING PEACE

from the SECOND INAUGURAL ADDRESS, *delivered by President Lincoln on March 4, 1865*

With malice toward none; with charity for all; with firmness in the right, as God gives us to see the right, let us strive on to finish the work we are in; to bind up the nation's wounds; to care for him who shall have borne the battle, and for his widow and his orphan—to do all which may achieve and cherish a just and lasting peace among ourselves and with all nations.

GO WEST, YOUNG MAN

by Horace Greeley, editor of the NEW YORK TRIBUNE, *1851*

The best business you can go into you will find on your father's farm or in his workshop. If you have no family or friends to aid you, and no prospect opened to you there, turn your face to the great West, and there build up a home and fortune.

GIT ALONG, LITTLE DOGIES

John A. and Alan Lomax chose this version of the old ballad sung by cowboys as a riding and range song since 1880 or earlier. A "dogie" is a motherless calf.

As I was a-walking one morning for pleasure,
I spied a cowpuncher come riding along;
His hat was throwed back and his spurs were a-jinglin',
As he approached me a-singin' this song,

CHORUS

Whoopee ti yi yo, git along, little dogies,
It's your misfortune, and none of my own.
Whoopee ti yi yo, git along, little dogies,
For you know Wyoming will be your new home.

Text from *Folk Song: U.S.A.*, copyright, 1947, by John A. and Alan Lomax, and published by Duell, Sloan & Pearce, Inc.

Early in the springtime we'll round up the dogies,
Slap on their brands and bob off their tails;
Round up our horses, load up the chuck-wagon,
Then throw those dogies up on the trail.

It's whooping and yelling and driving them dogies;
Oh, how I wish you would go on!
It's whooping and punching and go on, little dogies,
For you know Wyoming will be your new home.

Some boys goes up the trail for pleasure,
But that's where they git it most awfully wrong;
For you haven't any idea that trouble they give us
As we go driving those dogies along.

When the night comes on and we hold them on the bed-ground,
Those little dogies that roll on so slow;
Roll up the herd and cut out the strays,
And roll the little dogies that never rolled before.

Your mother she was raised way down in Texas,
Where the jimson weed and sand-burrs grow;
Now we'll fill you up on prickly pear and cholla
Till you're ready for the trail to Idaho.

Oh, you'll be soup for Uncle Sam's Injuns;
"It's beef, heap beef," I hear them cry.
Git along, git along, git along, little dogies,
You're going to be beef steers by and by.

THE RAILROAD CARS ARE COMING

old work song of the railroad builders

The great Pacific railway,
    For California hail!
Bring on the locomotive,
    Lay down the iron rail;
Across the rolling prairies
    By steam we're bound to go,
The railroad cars are coming, humming
    Through New Mexico,
The railroad cars are coming, humming
    Through New Mexico.

The little dogs in dog-town
    Will wag each little tail;
They'll think that something's coming
    A-riding on a rail.

The rattlesnake will show its fangs,
   The owl tu-whit, tu-who,
The railroad cars are coming, humming
   Through New Mexico,
The railroad cars are coming, humming
   Through New Mexico.

GIVE ME YOUR TIRED, YOUR POOR...

by Emma Lazarus. Published as THE NEW COLOSSUS, *in 1883, this sonnet is carved on a plaque at the base of the Statue of Liberty.*

Not like the brazen giant of Greek fame,
With conquering limbs astride from land to land;
Here at our sea-washed, sunset gates shall stand
A mighty woman with a torch, whose flame
Is the imprisoned lightning, and her name
Mother of Exiles. From her beacon-hand
Glows world-wide welcome; her mild eyes command
The air-bridged harbor that twin cities frame.
"Keep, ancient lands, your storied pomp!" cries she
With silent lips. "Give me your tired, your poor,
Your huddled masses yearning to breathe free,
The wretched refuse of your teeming shore.
Send these, the homeless, tempest-tost, to me,
I lift my lamp beside the golden door!"

THE MELTING POT

Israel Zangwill, an Englishman, wrote in his book, THE MELTING POT, *in 1908:*

America is God's Crucible, the great Melting Pot where all the races of Europe are melting and reforming! . . . God is making the American.

THE MARINES' HYMN

The first verse is very old, author unknown. The second and third verses were written by Colonel H. C. Davis in 1911.

From the Halls of Montezuma
To the shores of Tripoli
We fight our country's battles
On the land as on the sea.

First to fight for right and freedom
And to keep our honor clean;
We are proud to claim the title
Of United States Marines.

Our flag's unfurled to every breeze
From dawn to setting sun;
We have fought in every clime and place
Where we could take a gun.
In the snow of far-off Northern lands
And in sunny tropic scenes;
You will find us always on the job—
The United States Marines.

Here's health to you and to our Corps
Which we are proud to serve;
In many a strife we've fought for life
And never lost our nerve.
If the Army and the Navy
Ever look on Heaven's scenes,

They will find the streets are guarded
By United States Marines.

THE CAISSON SONG

by Major Edmund L. Gruber; written for the Second Battalion, Field Artillery, in the Philippines in 1908

Over hill, over dale, we have hit the dusty trail,
And those caissons go rolling along.
In and out, hear them shout, "Counter march and right about!"
And those caissons go rolling along.

CHORUS

Then it's hi! hi! hee! in the field artillery,
Sound off your numbers loud and strong.
Where e'er you go you will always know
That those caissons are rolling along.
Keep them rolling! And those caissons go rolling along.
Then it's Battery Halt!

Through the storm, through the night, up to where the doughboys fight,
All our caissons go rolling along.
At zero we'll be there, answering every call and flare,
While our caissons go rolling along.

Cavalry, boot to boot, we will join in the pursuit,
While the caissons go rolling along.
Action front, at a trot; volley fire with shell and shot,
While those caissons go rolling along.

ARMY BUGLE-CALL SONGS

authors unknown. Some of the songs were sung during the Civil War, or earlier.

Reveille

I can't get 'em up, I can't get 'em up,
I can't get 'em up in the morning.
I can't get 'em up, I can't get 'em up,
I can't get 'em up at all.
The corp'ral's worse than privates;
The sergeant's worse than corp'rals;
Lieutenant's worse than sergeants;
An' the captain's worst of all!

Sick Call

Come and get your quinine,
   And come and get your pills;
Oh! Come and get your quinine,
And cure, and cure,
   All your ills, and cure your ills.

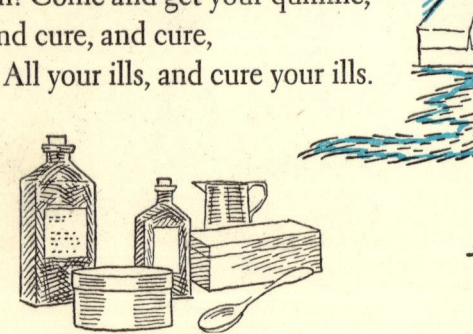

Mess Call

Soupy, soupy, soupy,
   Without a single bean;
Porky, porky, porky,
   Without a streak of lean;
Coffee, coffee, coffee,
   Without any cream.

Fatigue Call

With a pick and with a shovel, and with a hoe;
With a sentry at your back you won't say no;
With a pick and with a shovel, and with a hoe,
Down in the ditch you go!

Taps

Fading light
Dims the sight,
And a star gems the sky,
Drawing nigh,
From a-far,
Gleaming bright;
Falls the night.

THE FLAG GOES BY

by HENRY HOLCOMB BENNETT

   Hats off!
Along the street there comes
A blare of bugles, a ruffle of drums,
A flash of color beneath the sky:
   Hats off!
The flag is passing by!

Blue and crimson and white it shines,
Over the steel-tipped, ordered lines.
   Hats off!
The colors before us fly;
But more than the flag is passing by:
Sea-fights and land-fights, grim and great,
Fought to make and to save the State;
Weary marches and sinking ships;
Cheers of victory on dying lips;

Days of plenty and years of peace;
March of a strong land's swift increase;
Equal justice, right and law,
Stately honor and reverend awe;

Sign of a nation great and strong
To ward her people from foreign wrong;
Pride and glory and honor—all
Live in the colors to stand or fall.

Hats off!
Along the street there comes
A blare of bugles, a ruffle of drums;
And loyal hearts are beating high:
Hats off!
The flag is passing by!

AMERICA FOR ME

by HENRY VAN DYKE

'Tis fine to see the Old World, and travel up and down
Among the famous palaces and cities of renown,
To admire the crumbly castles and the statues of the kings—
But now I think I've had enough of antiquated things.

So it's home again, and home again, America for me!
My heart is turning home again, and there I long to be,
In the land of youth and freedom beyond the ocean bars,
Where the air is full of sunlight and the flag is full of stars.

Oh, London is a man's town, there's power in the air;
And Paris is a woman's town, with flowers in her hair;
And it's sweet to dream in Venice, and it's great to study Rome;
But when it comes to living there is no place like home.

Reprinted with the permission of Charles Scribner's Sons from THE POEMS OF HENRY VAN DYKE by Henry Van Dyke, copyright 1911 Charles Scribner's Sons; renewal copyright 1939 Tertius Van Dyke.

I like the German fir-woods, in green battalions drilled;
I like the gardens of Versailles, with dashing fountains filled;
But, oh, to take your hand, my dear, and ramble for a day
In the friendly western woodland where Nature has her way!

I know that Europe's wonderful, yet something seems to lack:
The Past is too much with her, and the people looking back.
But the glory of the Present is to make the Future free—
We love our land for what she is and what she is to be.

Oh, it's home again, and home again, America for me!
I want a ship that's westward bound to plough the rolling sea,
To the blessed Land of Room Enough beyond the ocean bars,
Where the air is full of sunshine and the flag is full of stars.

The Star-Spangled Banner

by FRANCIS SCOTT KEY

illustrated by PHOEBE ERICKSON

O say, can you see, by the dawn's early
Whose broad stripes and bright stars, through the perilous

light, What so proudly we hailed at the
fight, O'er the ramparts we watched were so

twilight's last gleaming?
gallantly streaming! And the

FORT McHENRY

rock-ets' red glare, the bombs burst-ing in air, Gave proof through the night that our flag was still there: O say, does that star-span-gled ban-ner yet wave O'er the land of the free and the home of the brave?

O say, can you see, by the dawn's early light,
What so proudly we hailed at the twilight's last gleaming?
Whose broad stripes and bright stars, through the perilous fight,
O'er the ramparts we watched were so gallantly streaming!
And the rockets' red glare, the bombs bursting in air,
Gave proof through the night that our flag was still there:
O say, does that star-spangled banner yet wave
O'er the land of the free and the home of the brave?

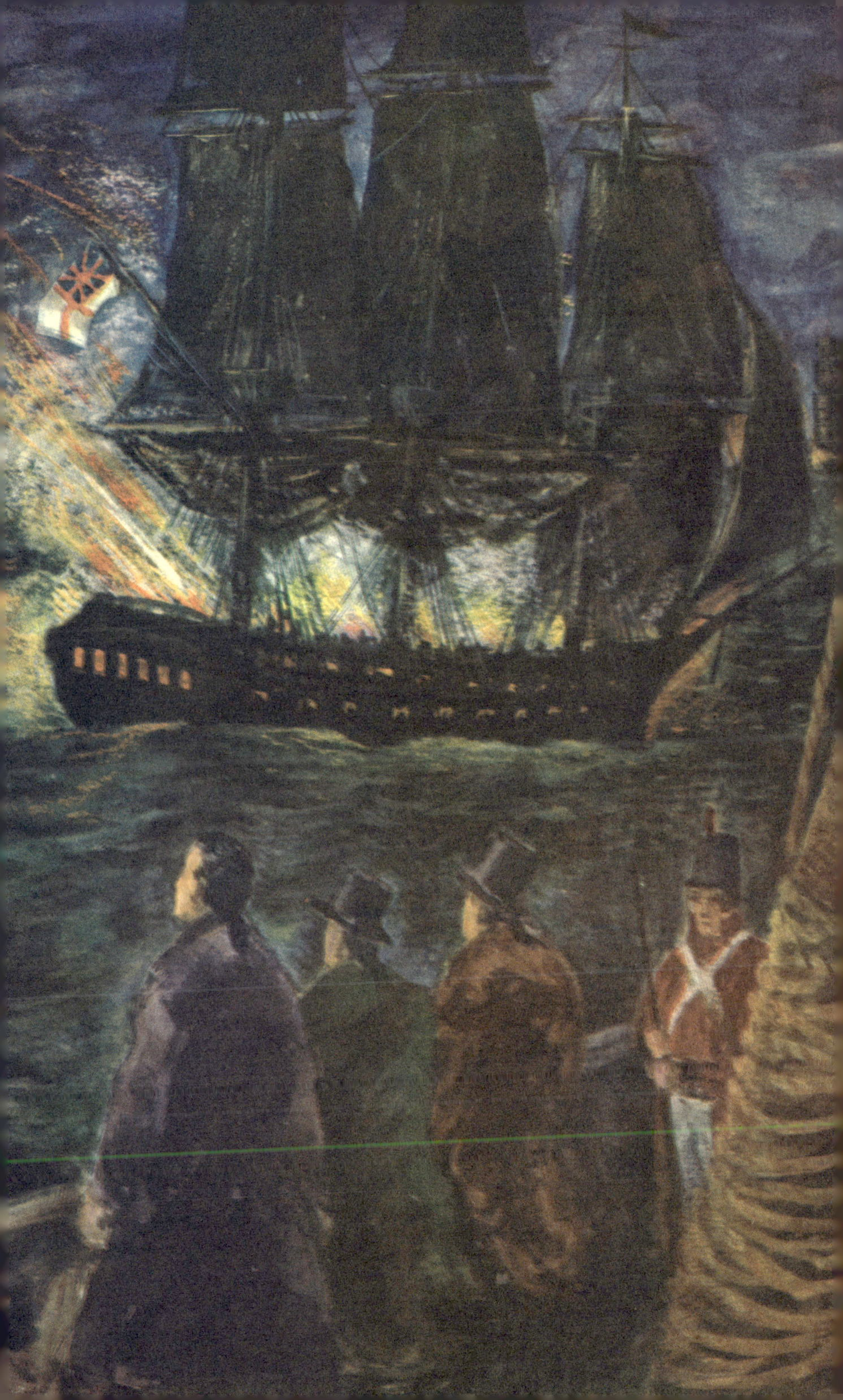

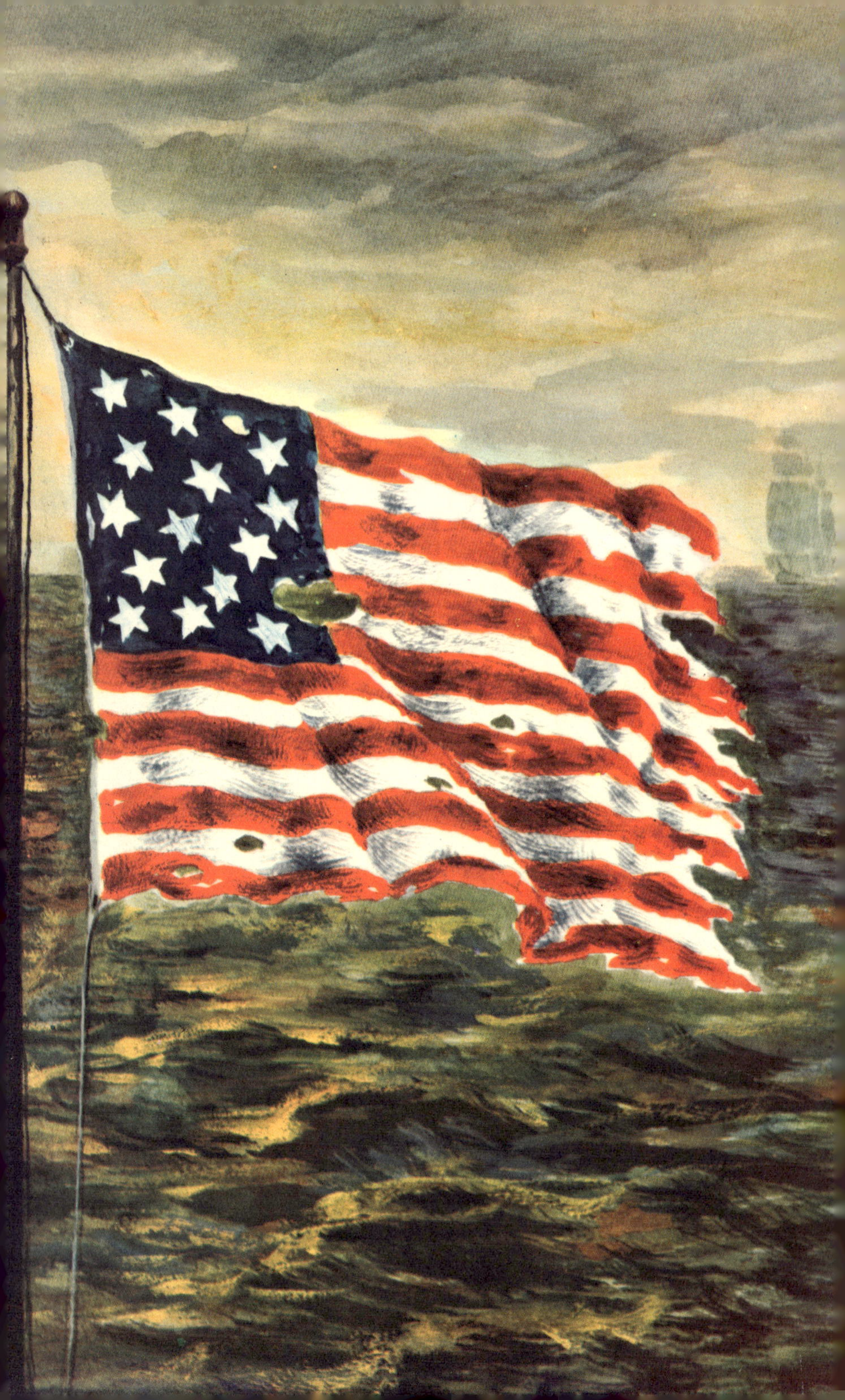

On the shore, dimly seen through the mists of the deep,
Where the foe's haughty host in dread silence reposes,
What is that which the breeze, o'er the towering steep,
   As it fitfully blows, half conceals, half discloses?
Now it catches the gleam of the morning's first beam,
In full glory reflected now shines on the stream:
   'Tis the star-spangled banner! O long may it wave
   O'er the land of the free and the home of the brave!

And where is that band who so vauntingly swore
That the havoc of war and the battle's confusion
A home and a country should leave us no more?
Their blood has washed out their foul footsteps' pollution.
No refuge could save the hireling and slave
From the terror of flight, or the gloom of the grave:
And the star-spangled banner in triumph doth wave
O'er the land of the free and the home of the brave!

O thus be it ever, when freemen shall stand
Between their loved homes and the war's desolation!
Blest with victory and peace, may the heaven-rescued land
Praise the Power that hath made and preserved us a nation.

Then conquer we must, when our cause it is just,
And this be our motto: "In God is our trust."
And the star-spangled banner in triumph shall wave
O'er the land of the free and the home of the brave!

Pet of the Met

written and illustrated by
LYDIA *and* DON FREEMAN

High up in the attic of the Metropolitan Opera House, in a forgotten harp case, there once lived a white mouse named Maestro Petrini.

With him lived Madame Petrini and their three teeny-weeny Petrinis, Doe, Ray, and Mee.

Copyright, 1953, by Lydia and Don Freeman, and published by The Viking Press, Inc.

Next to his family Maestro Petrini loved the opera more than anything else in the world. He knew all the opera stories by heart and could hum most of the music.

This was not surprising because he worked for his daily cheese downstairs in the Opera House itself.

Here he is, working as a page-turner for the Prompter in the Prompter's box.

The Prompter's box is a small cavelike place set in the center of the stage footlights. No one in the audience ever sees or hears the Prompter, but he is a very important man. The singers watch and listen to him, for they depend upon him to help them remember the words of their songs if they should ever forget.

The Prompter was always careful to keep Maestro Petrini well hidden behind the big music book, and for two good reasons: first, singers are not exactly partial to mice; and second, the Prompter knew of a certain cat, named Mefisto, who lived in the basement just below. Mefisto lived in an empty violin case, but he hated music more than anything else in the world, except mice.

Every time he heard singing from upstairs he would try to shut out the sound. He wouldn't even let himself listen to find out whether or not he liked it. He was just plain prejudiced against music.

Every night after the performance it was his job to rid the great Opera House of mice. This is how he earned his daily bowl of milk. It was an easy job because he never found any victims.

The Opera House was so enormous that Mefisto had never discovered the attic high at the top. This was fortunate for the carefree Petrinis.

During his spare time Maestro Petrini would put on his own opera performances with his family as the cast. Of all the operas their favorite was *The Magic Flute* by Mozart.

The Magic Flute is about a prince who, with a magic flute to protect him, searches for his princess throughout the realm of the Queen of the Night. A funny birdcatcher named Papageno helps him to find his way. Whenever they are in danger the music of the magic flute charms even the most ferocious animals of the forest. This is how they are able to make their way safely through every trial.

Maestro Petrini took great delight in playing the part of the foolish birdcatcher. Madame Petrini had made his costume out of an old feather duster she had found in the corner of the attic.

Madame Petrini herself preferred to play the Queen of the Night. She made her costume out of some dark-blue cheesecloth she just happened to have handy.

The scene they all liked best was the one in which the ferocious animals of the forest dance to the music of the magic flute. You can imagine who whistled like a flute!

For this scene Doe dressed up as a lion by wearing a mop and tying a tassel to the end of his tail. Ray became a rabbit by folding back his ears and tying his tail into a bunny-knot. As for Mee, he merely put on his mother's green spectacles, and painted stripes around his tail. You couldn't tell him from a tiger!

They danced this scene so hard and so long that they never were able to finish the rest of the opera, no matter how early they had started.

One day just after an especially wonderful dancing scene, the teeny-weeny Petrinis gathered around their papa and breathlessly pleaded, "Please, Papa, when can we go downstairs and see you act in the real opera?"

That very evening as they sat down to an elegant cheese-soufflé supper, Papa Petrini gave his family a surprise and a promise. They would all be permitted to attend a Special Children's Opera matinee the next day. It was to be *The Magic Flute!*

First thing the next morning Madame Petrini set about washing everybody's ears. She wanted to make sure that not a single note would be missed!

Maestro Petrini combed his hair and curled his whiskers, a process which took most of the morning.

Meanwhile, downstairs, Mefisto, the cat, suspected that something extraordinary was going on that afternoon. He went prowling around backstage, searching for you know who! When he peeked through the peephole in the curtain this is what he saw. The children were already beginning to arrive for the matinee!

Upstairs in the attic at this very moment the Petrinis were setting out, all primped and powdered and on their best behavior.

Maestro Petrini had to let his family find their own seats while he hurried off to his Prompter's box to get ready for the performance.

Soon every seat in the entire Opera House was filled. But where are Madame Petrini and Doe, Ray, Mee?

Here they are! They have found themselves a perfect place. What could be better than to snuggle behind a young lady's white gloves?

Gradually the lights all over the house dimmed down. Everyone was silent and expectant.

The orchestra conductor appeared and made one long deep bow.

Then the overture began.

Just before the great golden curtains parted, the Prompter leaned over and whispered into his partner's ear, "We must be especially good today, my pet. Boys and girls deserve the very best, you know!"

Then the curtain went up. The opera was under way!

When Papageno, the foolish birdcatcher, appeared and began to sing, the audience was all eyes and ears.

And when the Prince played upon his flute, one by one the stage animals came out and danced to the magic music.

But look! Can it be? Yes, it is! Maestro Petrini, completely carried away by the music, has leaped out of his box before the Prompter can stop him!

He's dancing! And what's more, he is dancing in perfect rhythm to the music!

Of course none of the children in the audience can see the tiny Maestro dancing. But his family can. They are taking turns looking through a pair of opera glasses left resting on the velvet railing. And to tell the awful truth, someone else is watching! The cat, Mefisto! He watches from the dark side-curtains backstage!

"Petrini! Run for your life!" shouts the Prompter.

Out springs Mefisto.

In and out about the stage Mefisto chases Petrini. Through the dancers' legs they speed like streaks of lightning, while the flute music grows more and more beautiful and exciting until poor Petrini is caught by his coat tail! But wait—

The strangest thing is happening. What can it be?

Mefisto is suddenly beginning to feel and look different. He is falling under the spell of the flute music!

Now *he*'s dancing! And dancing! Never in the history of the Metropolitan has there been such a scene—such waltzing and turning—such feline grace!

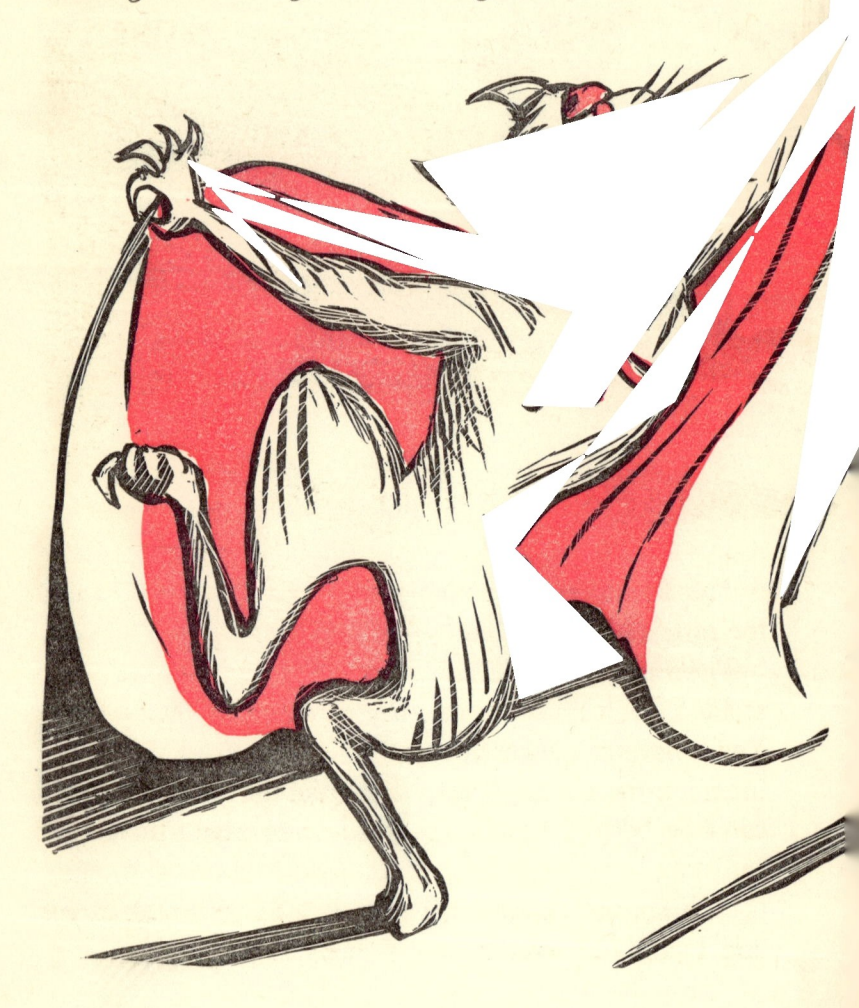

Even after the music had stopped, Mefisto and Petrini continued to whirl and twirl until the curtain had to be brought down.

When the audience called for more, Maestro Petrini felt obliged to step out in front of the curtain and make several deep, dignified bows.

The Prompter reached out and pulled him back into the box. This broke the spell for Petrini.

The Prompter was very angry. "See here, my pet," he scolded, "you made me lose my place in the music book. You'll have to decide now, once and for all, whether you intend to be an opera star or a page-turner. You simply can't be both! I have a good notion to hire Mefisto the cat."

"Oh no, no!" pleaded Petrini. "I'll be your page-turner and I promise never to be an opera star again!"

That afternoon when the performance was over, a subdued and humbled Maestro returned to his home in the harp case. There, to his great surprise, his family showered him with bravos and squeals of applause! They told him his performance had been the best part of the opera!

"And the cat was pretty funny, too!" said Doe. "The flute certainly tamed him down—and just in the nick of time!" To this remark Papa Petrini said nothing. He was hungry. And he had brought home a special present from

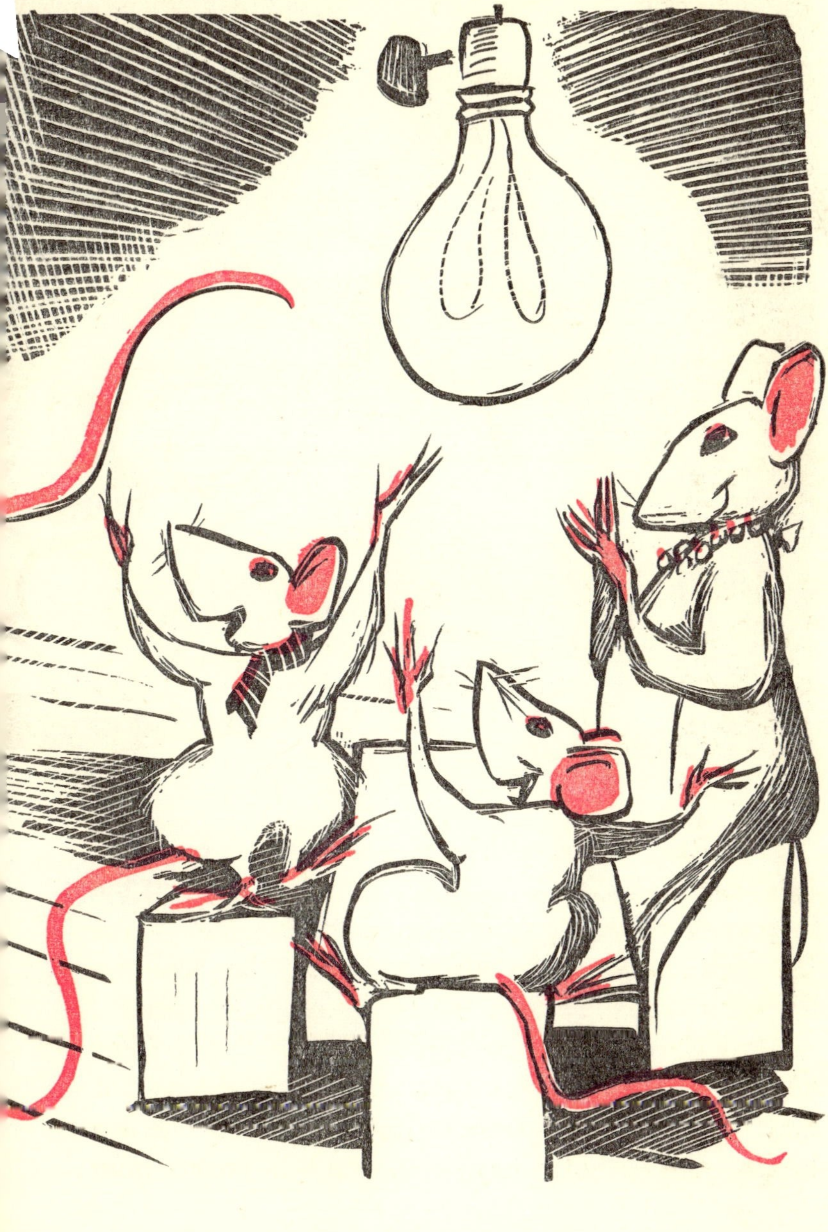

his friend the Prompter—an extra-large portion of Swiss cheese!

Far down in the basement another opera lover was exhausted but happy. Mefisto, forgetting for the first time about ridding the house of mice, had his supper and went straight to bed in his violin case. He purred himself to sleep with a tune from *The Magic Flute*.

As you might guess, Maestro Petrini and Mister Mefisto soon became good friends. And to this day it is said that between them they have the run of the entire Metropolitan Opera House!

The Tinder Box

by HANS CHRISTIAN ANDERSEN

illustrated by ELIZABETH SKILTON

A soldier came marching along the highroad. One, two! One, two! He had his knapsack on his back and his sword at his side, for he had

Text from *Hans Andersen's Fairy Tales*, translated by Mrs. Edgar Lucas. Children's Illustrated Classics. Reprinted by permission of the publishers, E. P. Dutton & Company, Inc.

been to the wars, and he was on his way home now. He met an old witch on the road; she was so ugly her lower lip hung right down onto her chin.

She said: "Good evening, soldier! What a nice sword you've got, and such a big knapsack; you are a real soldier! You shall have as much money as ever you like!"

"Thank you kindly, you old witch!" said the soldier.

"Do you see that big tree?" said the witch, pointing to a tree close by. "It is hollow inside! Climb up to the top and you will see a hole into which you can let yourself down, right down under the tree! I will tie a rope round your waist so that I can haul you up again when you call!"

"What am I to do down under the tree?" asked the soldier.

"Fetch money!" said the witch. "You must know that when you get down to the bottom of the tree you will find yourself in a wide passage; it's quite light there, for there are over a hundred blazing lamps. You will see three doors which you can open, for the keys are there. If you go into the first room you will see a big box in the middle of the floor. A dog is sitting on the top of it, and he has eyes as big as saucers, but you needn't mind that. I will give you my blue-checked apron, which you can spread out on the floor; then go quickly forward, take up the dog and put him on my apron, open the box and take out as much money as ever you like. It is all copper, but if you like silver better, go into the next room. There you will find a dog with eyes as big as millstones; but never mind that, put him on my apron and take the money. If you prefer gold you can have it too, and as much as you can carry, if you go into the third room. But the dog sitting on that box has eyes each as big as the Round Tower in Copenhagen. He *is* a dog, indeed, as you may imagine! But don't let it trouble you; you only have to put him onto my apron and then he won't hurt you, and you can take as much gold out of the box as you like!"

"That's not so bad!" said the soldier. "But what am I to give you, old witch? For you'll want something, I'll be bound."

"No," said the witch, "not a single penny do I want; I only want you to bring me an old tinder box that my grandmother forgot the last time she was down there!"

"Well, tie the rope round my waist!" said the soldier.

"Here it is," said the witch, "and here is my blue-checked apron."

Then the soldier climbed up the tree, let himself slide down the hollow trunk, and found himself, as the witch had said, in the wide passage where the many hundred lamps were burning.

Now he opened the first door. Ugh! There sat the dog

with eyes as big as saucers staring at him.

"You are a nice fellow!" said the soldier, as he put him onto the witch's apron, and took out as many pennies as he could cram into his pockets. Then he shut the box, and put the dog on the top of it again, and went into the next room. Hallo! There sat the dog with eyes as big as millstones.

"You shouldn't stare at me so hard; you might get a pain in your eyes!" Then he put the dog on the apron, but when he saw all the silver in the box he threw away all the coppers, and stuffed his pockets and his knapsack with silver. Then he went into the third room. Oh, how horrible! That dog really had two eyes as big as the Round Tower, and they rolled round and round like wheels.

"Good evening!" said the soldier, saluting, for he had never seen such a dog in his life; but after looking at him for a bit he thought: "That will do," and then he lifted him down onto the apron and opened the chest. Preserve us! What a lot of gold! He could buy the whole of Copenhagen with it, and all the sugar pigs from the cake-woman, all the tin soldiers, whips, and rocking horses in the world! That was money indeed! Now the soldier threw away all the silver he had filled his pockets and his knapsack with, and put gold in its place. Yes, he crammed all his pockets, his knapsack, his cap, and his boots so full that he could hardly walk! Now he really had got a lot of money. He put the dog back onto the box, shut the door, and shouted up through the tree: "Haul me up, you old witch!"

"Have you got the tinder box?"

"Oh, to be sure!" said the soldier. "I had quite forgotten

it." And he went back to fetch it. The witch hauled him up, and there he was standing on the highroad again with his pockets, boots, knapsack, and cap full of gold.

"What do you want the tinder box for?" asked the soldier.

"That's no business of yours," said the witch. "You've got the money; give me the tinder box!"

"Rubbish!" said the soldier. "Tell me directly what you want with it, or I will draw my sword and cut off your head."

"I won't!" said the witch.

Then the soldier cut off her head; there she lay! But he tied all the money up in her apron, slung it on his back like a pack, put the tinder box in his pocket, and marched off to the town.

It was a beautiful town, and he went straight to the finest hotel, ordered the grandest rooms and all the food he liked best, because he was a rich man now that he had so much money.

Certainly the servant who had to clean his boots thought they were funny old things for such a rich gentleman, but he had not had time yet to buy any new ones; the next day he bought new boots and fine clothes. The soldier now became a fine gentleman, and the people told him all about the grand things in the town, and about their king, and what a lovely princess his daughter was.

"Where is she to be seen?" asked the soldier.

"You can't see her at all!" they all said. "She lives in a great copper castle surrounded with walls and towers. Nobody but the king dare go in and out, for it has been prophesied that she will marry a common soldier, and the king doesn't like that!"

"I should like to see her well enough!" thought the soldier. But there was no way of getting leave for that.

He now led a very merry life; went to theatres, drove about in the king's park, and gave away a lot of money to poor people, which was very nice of him; for he remembered how disagreeable it used to be not to have a penny in his pocket. Now he was rich, wore fine clothes, and had a great many friends, who all said what a nice fellow he was —a thorough gentleman—and he liked to be told that.

But as he went on spending money every day and his store was never renewed, he at last found himself with only twopence left. Then he was obliged to move out of his fine rooms. He had to take a tiny little attic up under the roof, clean his own boots, and mend them himself with a darning needle. None of his friends went to see him because there were far too many stairs.

One dark evening when he had not even enough money to buy a candle with, he suddenly remembered that there was a little bit in the old tinder box he had brought out of the hollow tree, when the witch helped him down. He got out the tinder box with the candle end in it and struck fire, but as the sparks flew out from the flint the door burst open and the dog with eyes as big as saucers, which he had seen down under the tree, stood before him and said: "What does my lord command?"

"By heaven!" said the soldier, "this is a nice kind of tinder box, if I can get whatever I want like this! Get me some money," he said to the dog, and away it went.

It was back in a twinkling with a big bag full of pennies in its mouth.

Now the soldier saw what a treasure he had in the tinder box. If he struck once, the dog which sat on the box of copper came; if he struck twice, there was the dog on the silver box; and if he struck three times, the one from the box of gold appeared.

He now moved down to the grand rooms and got his fine clothes again, and then all his friends knew him once more, and liked him as much as ever.

Then he suddenly began to think: "After all, it's a curious thing that no man can get a sight of the princess! Everyone says she is so beautiful! But what is the good of that when she always has to be shut up in that big copper palace with all the towers. Can I not somehow manage to see her? Where is my tinder box?" Then he struck the flint and, whisk, came the dog with eyes as big as saucers.

"It certainly is the middle of the night," said the soldier, "but I am very anxious to see the princess, if only for a single moment."

The dog was out of the door in an instant, and before the soldier had time to think about it he was back again with the princess. There she was, fast asleep on the dog's back, and she was so lovely that anybody could see that she must be a real princess! The soldier could not help it, but he was obliged to kiss her, for he was a true soldier.

Then the dog ran back again with the princess, but in the morning, when the king and queen were having breakfast, the princess said that she had had such a wonderful dream about a dog and a soldier. She had ridden on the dog's back, and the soldier had kissed her.

"That's a pretty tale," said the queen.

After this an old lady in waiting had to sit by her bed at night to see if this was really a dream, or what it could be.

The soldier longed so intensely to see the princess again that at night the dog came to fetch her. He took her up and ran off with her as fast as he could, but the old lady in waiting put on her galoshes and ran just as fast behind them; when she saw that they disappeared into a large house she thought "Now I know where it is," and made a big cross with chalk on the gate. Then she went home and lay down, and presently the dog came back, too, with the princess. When he saw that there was a cross on the gate he took a bit of chalk, too, and made crosses on all the gates in the town; now this was very clever of him, for the lady in waiting could not possibly find the gate when there were crosses on all the gates.

Early next morning the king, the queen, the lady in waiting, and all the court officials went to see where the princess had been.

"There it is," said the king, when he saw the first door with the cross on it.

"No, my dear husband, it is there," said the queen, who saw another door with a cross on it.

"But there is one, and there is another!" they all cried out.

They soon saw that it was hopeless to try and find it.

Now the queen was a very clever woman; she knew more than how to drive in a chariot. She took her big gold scissors and cut up a large piece of silk into small pieces, and made a pretty little bag, which she filled with fine grains of buckwheat. She then tied it onto the back of the princess, and when that was done she cut a little hole in the bag so that the grains could drop out all the way wherever the princess went.

At night the dog came again, took the princess on his back, and ran off with her to the soldier, who was so fond of her that he longed to be a prince, so that he might have her for his wife.

The dog never noticed how the grain dropped out all along the road from the palace to the soldier's window, where he ran up the wall with the princess.

In the morning the king and the queen easily saw where their daughter had been, and they seized the soldier and threw him into the dungeons.

There he lay! Oh, how dark and tiresome it was. And then one day they said to him: "Tomorrow you are to be hanged." It was not amusing to be told that, especially as he had left his tinder box behind him at the hotel.

In the morning he could see through the bars in the little window that the people were hurrying out of the town to see him hanged. He heard the drums, and saw the soldiers marching along. All the world was going; among them was a shoemaker's boy in his leather apron and slippers. He was in such a hurry that he lost one of his slippers, and it fell close under the soldier's window where he was peeping out through the bars.

"I say, you boy! Don't be in such a hurry," said the soldier to him. "Nothing will happen till I get there! But if you will run to the house where I used to live, and fetch me my tinder box, you shall have a penny! You must put your best foot foremost!"

The boy was only too glad to have the penny, and tore off to get the tinder box, gave it to the soldier, and—yes, now we shall hear.

Outside the town a high scaffold had been raised, and the soldiers were drawn up round about it, as well as crowds of the townspeople. The king and the queen sat upon a beautiful throne exactly opposite the judge and all the councillors.

The soldier mounted the ladder, but when they were about to put the rope round his neck he said that before undergoing his punishment a criminal was always allowed the gratification of a harmless wish, and he wanted very much to smoke a pipe, as it would be his last pipe in this world.

The king would not deny him this, so the soldier took out his tinder box and struck fire, once, twice, three times, and there were all the dogs. The one with eyes like saucers, the one with eyes like millstones, and the one whose eyes were as big as the Round Tower.

"Help me! Save me from being hanged!" cried the soldier.

And then the dogs rushed at the soldiers and the councillors; they took one by the legs, and another by the nose, and threw them up many fathoms into the air; and when they fell down they were broken all to pieces.

"I won't!" cried the king, but the biggest dog took both him and the queen and threw them after all the others. Then the soldiers became alarmed, and the people shouted: "Oh, good soldier, you shall be our king, and marry the beautiful princess!"

Then they conducted the soldier to the king's chariot, and all three dogs danced along in front of him and shouted "Hurrah!" The boys all put their fingers in their mouths and whistled, and the soldiers presented arms. The princess came out of the copper palace and became queen, which pleased her very much. The wedding took place in a week, and the dogs all had seats at the table, where they sat staring with all their eyes.

Pandora

A *Greek Legend*

illustrated by COLLEEN BROWNING

Text based on "The Paradise of Children," from *A Wonder Book*, by Nathaniel Hawthorne.

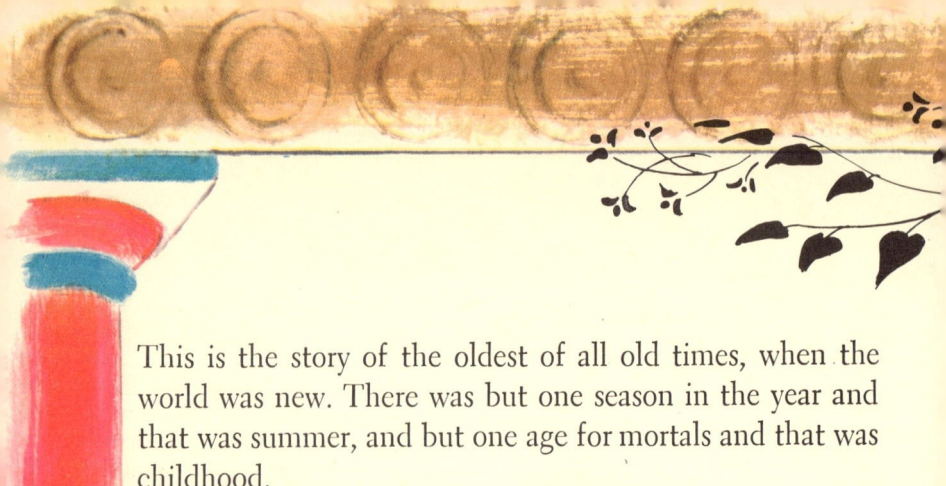

This is the story of the oldest of all old times, when the world was new. There was but one season in the year and that was summer, and but one age for mortals and that was childhood.

In this Paradise of Children there dwelt a boy named Epimetheus. Because he lived alone, the gods on Mount Olympus sent down another child to live and play with him. Her name was Pandora.

Pandora was lively, pretty, happy and good. But she had one great fault: she was extremely curious. The very first time she stepped through the door of Epimetheus' little house, she spied a large carved chest and wanted to know immediately what was in it.

When Epimetheus told her that the chest had been brought to him by the god Mercury, who had left it in the house with strict instructions *never to open the chest, never even to unlock it*, Pandora was more curious than ever.

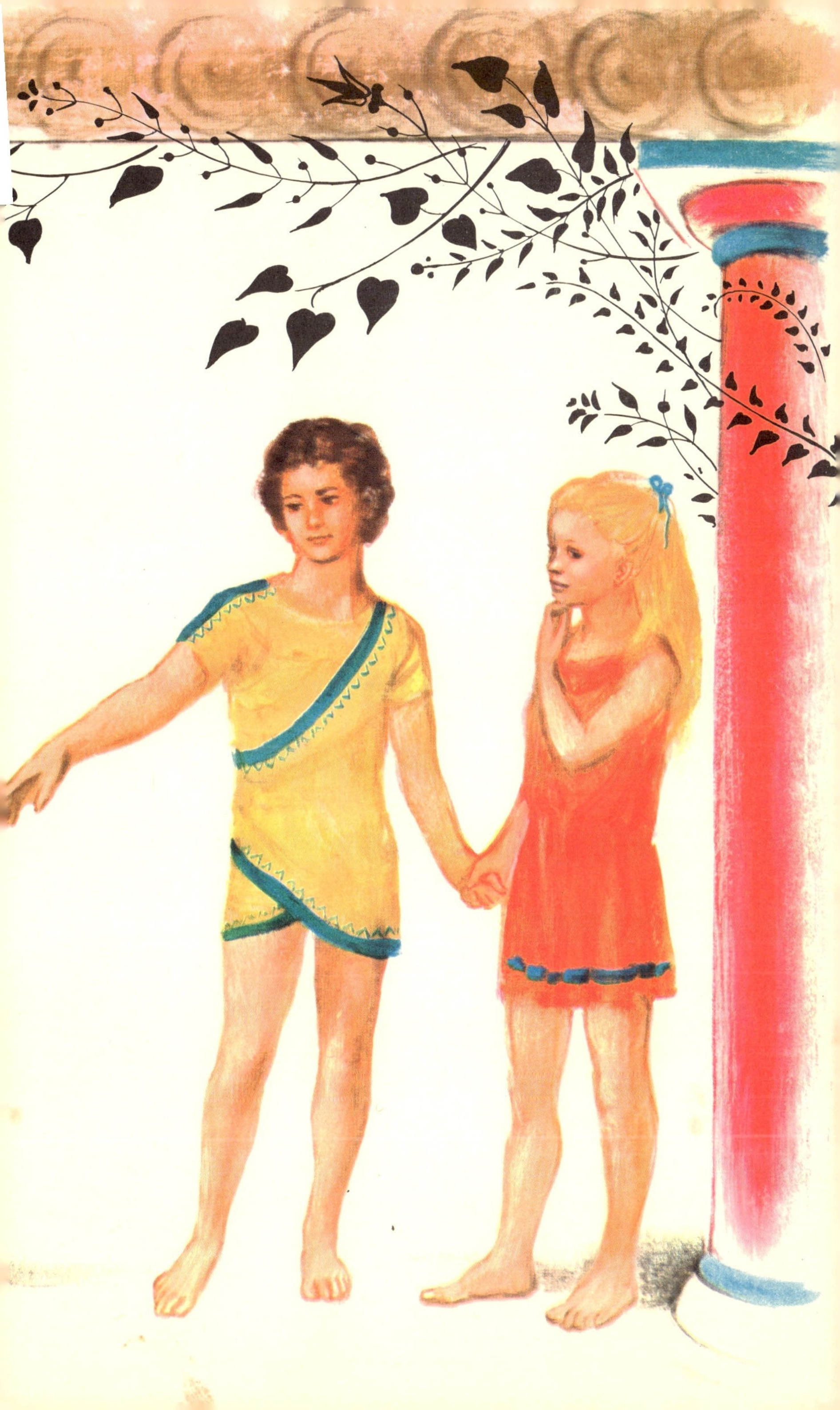

"How silly!" she complained. "Why can't we just peek in the chest? We wouldn't touch a thing that was inside."

But Epimetheus was so horrified at the idea of disobeying the god Mercury, that Pandora decided it was best to join the boy in play in the beautiful Paradise, and say no more about the mysterious carved chest.

And what wonderful times the children had in those days! There were no grownups and no schools. There was always plenty to eat: fruits and nuts and milk and honey. No one was ever sick or sad or angry. The truth is, those ugly monsters called Troubles had never been seen on the earth.

But do you think Pandora was happy? Every day she thought more and more about the locked chest, and every day her curiosity grew sharper.

"What is inside?" she wondered. "Toys? Jewels? Pretty clothes?"

And every day Epimetheus' stubbornness in not allowing her to open the chest seemed sillier and sillier to Pandora.

"What harm could it do?" she would whisper to herself. "Who would ever know if I did just *peek* inside?"

Then one day, Pandora was alone in the little house, for Epimetheus had gone into the woods to gather chestnuts. For the hundredth time the girl studied the curious golden knot that served to lock the chest.

"I'll just untwist it a little," Pandora thought. "It's tangled so. It can't hurt to untangle it a little."

She worked at the knot, untwining a bit here, a bit there, when—suddenly—the knot untangled itself and became two straight, thick golden ropes.

"Oh, what will Epimetheus say when he sees the knot undone? I shall have to twist it up again, before he gets home. But—but—suppose, first, I just lift the lid a tiny, tiny crack. No one will even guess."

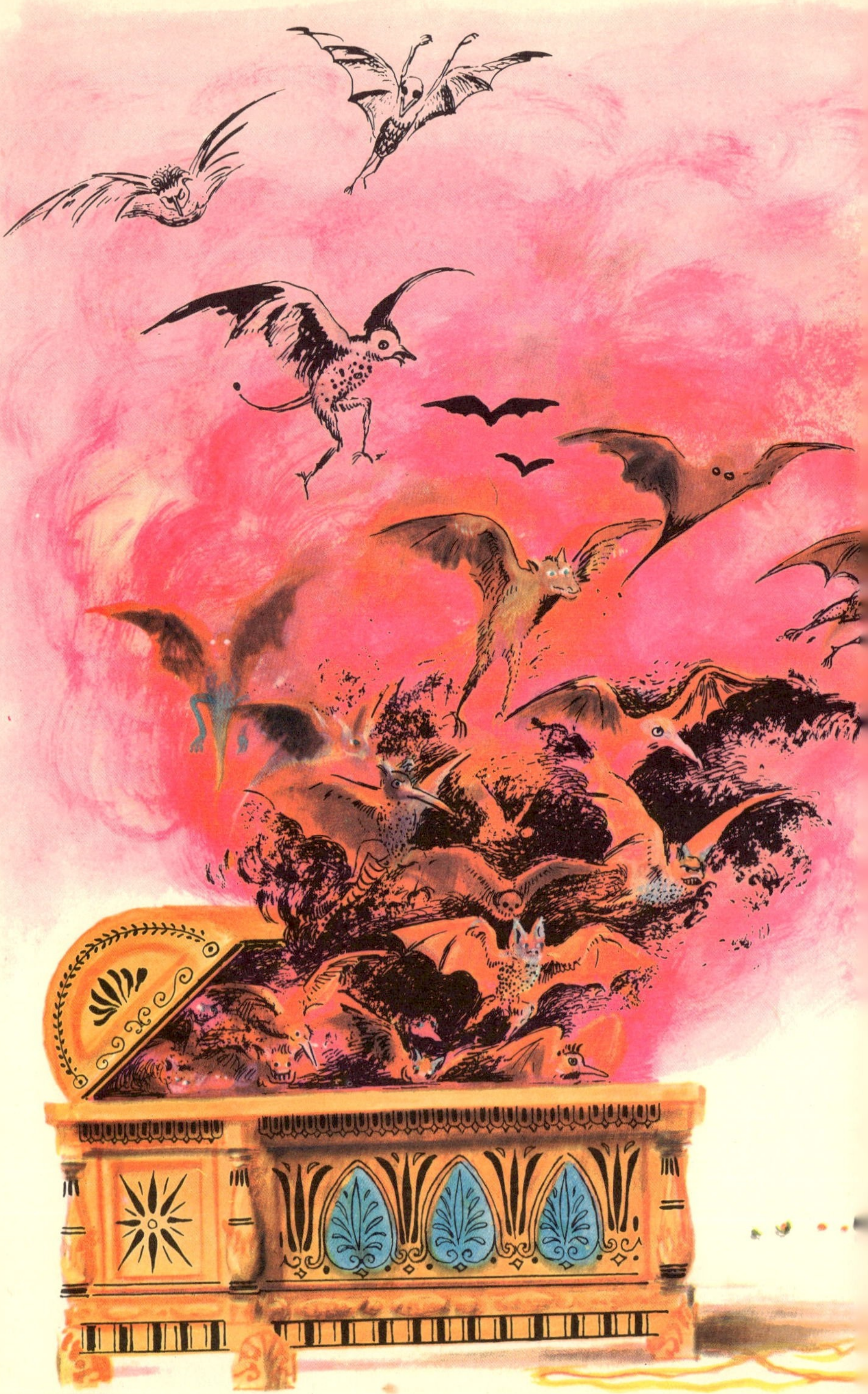

And kneeling before the chest, Pandora raised the lid.

There was a great clap of thunder; the room grew dark; and from the chest there came a hot, rushing wind. A sudden swarm of horrid, batlike creatures rushed past her, while, at the same instant, she heard the voice of Epimetheus crying:

"Pandora! Pandora! You have opened the chest! What have you let out?"

And indeed—what had Pandora allowed to escape into the world? It was some time before the children came to know that the ugly winged creatures were the whole family of human Troubles: anger, sorrow, sickness, despair. In short, everything that makes us unhappy had been shut in that mysterious chest. Had it not been for Pandora's curiosity, no child would have had cause to shed a single tear from that hour to this moment.

But one thing Pandora and Epimetheus did not know: still within the chest was one small creature. As soon as she fluttered out into the darkened room, the Troubles flew out the doors and windows; the sunshine entered the house again; and Pandora and Epimetheus lost their fear. So because of that last tiny creature, this boy and girl learned to work and grow up cheerfully in a world which was no longer the Paradise of Children.

For the small creature was Hope; and from that day to this, when people are saddened or frightened by the Troubles, lovely Hope comes to them to lighten their hearts.

The Velveteen Rabbit

by MARGERY WILLIAMS

illustrated by MAURICE SENDAK

There was once a velveteen rabbit, and in the beginning he was really splendid. He was fat and bunchy, as a rabbit should be; his coat was spotted brown and white, he had real thread whiskers, and his ears were lined with pink sateen. On Christmas morning, when he sat wedged in the top of the Boy's stocking, with a sprig of holly between his paws, the effect was charming.

Reprinted by permission of Doubleday & Company, Inc.

There were other things in the stocking, nuts and oranges and a toy engine, and chocolate almonds and a clockwork mouse, but the Rabbit was quite the best of all. For at least two hours the Boy loved him, and then Aunts and Uncles came to dinner, and there was a great rustling of tissue paper and unwrapping of parcels, and in the excitement of looking at all the new presents the Velveteen Rabbit was forgotten.

For a long time he lived in the toy cupboard or on the nursery floor, and no one thought very much about him. He was naturally shy, and being only made of velveteen, some of the more expensive toys quite snubbed him. The mechanical toys were very superior, and looked down upon everyone else; they were full of modern ideas, and pretended they were real. The model boat, who had lived through two seasons and lost most of his paint, caught the tone from them and never missed an opportunity of referring to his rigging in technical terms. The Rabbit could not claim to be a model of anything, for he didn't know that real rabbits existed; he thought they were all stuffed with sawdust like himself, and he understood that sawdust was quite out-of-date and should never be mentioned in modern circles. Even Timothy, the jointed wooden lion, who was made by the disabled soldiers, and should have had broader views, put on airs and pretended he was connected with Government. Between them all, the poor little Rabbit was made to feel himself very insignificant and commonplace; and the only person who was kind to him at all was the Skin Horse.

The Skin Horse had lived longer in the nursery than

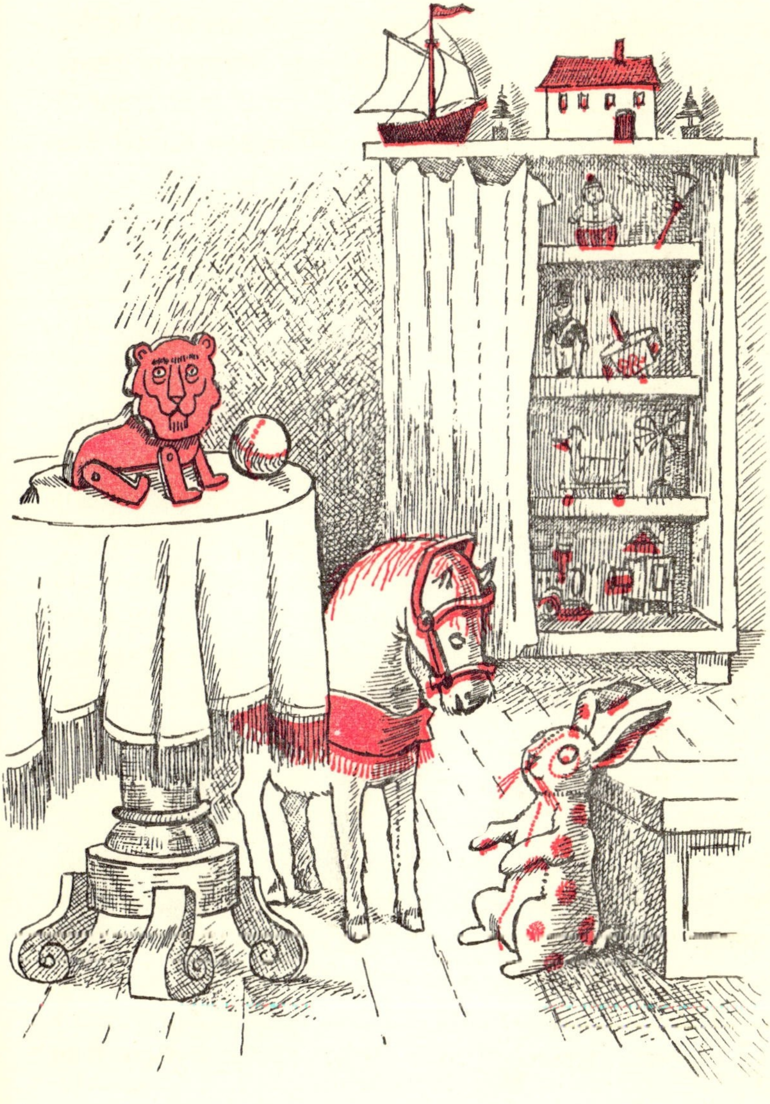

any of the others. He was so old that his brown coat was bald in patches and showed the seams underneath, and most of the hairs in his tail had been pulled out to string bead necklaces. He was wise, for he had seen a long succession of mechanical toys arrive to boast and swagger, and by-and-by break their mainsprings and pass away, and he knew that they were only toys, and would never turn into anything else. For nursery magic is very strange and wonderful, and only those playthings that are old and wise and experienced like the Skin Horse understand all about it.

"What is REAL?" asked the Rabbit one day, when they were lying side by side near the nursery fender, before Nana came to tidy the room. "Does it mean having things that buzz inside you and a stick-out handle?"

"Real isn't how you are made," said the Skin Horse. "It's a thing that happens to you. When a child loves you for a long, long time, not just to play with, but REALLY loves you, then you become Real."

"Does it hurt?" asked the Rabbit.

"Sometimes," said the Skin Horse, for he was always truthful. "When you are Real you don't mind being hurt."

"Does it happen all at once, like being wound up," he asked, "or bit by bit?"

"It doesn't happen all at once," said the Skin Horse. "You become. It takes a long time. That's why it doesn't often happen to people who break easily, or have sharp edges, or who have to be carefully kept. Generally, by the time you are Real, most of your hair has been loved off, and your eyes drop out and you get loose in the joints and very shabby. But these things don't matter at all, because once you are Real you can't be ugly, except to people who don't understand."

"I suppose *you* are Real?" said the Rabbit. And then he wished he had not said it, for he thought the Skin Horse might be sensitive. But the Skin Horse only smiled.

"The Boy's Uncle made me Real," he said. "That was a great many years ago; but once you are Real you can't become unreal again. It lasts for always."

The Rabbit sighed. He thought it would be a long time

before this magic called Real happened to him. He longed to become Real, to know what it felt like; and yet the idea of growing shabby and losing his eyes and whiskers was rather sad. He wished that he could become it without these uncomfortable things happening to him.

There was a person called Nana who ruled the nursery. Sometimes she took no notice of the playthings lying about, and sometimes, for no reason whatever, she went swooping about like a great wind and hustled them away in cupboards. She called this "tidying up," and the playthings all hated it, especially the tin ones. The Rabbit didn't mind it so much, for wherever he was thrown he came down soft.

One evening, when the Boy was going to bed, he couldn't find the china dog that always slept with him. Nana was in a hurry, and it was too much trouble to hunt for china dogs at bedtime, so she simply looked about her, and seeing that the toy cupboard door stood open, she made a swoop.

"Here," she said, "take your old Bunny! He'll do to sleep with you!" And she dragged the Rabbit out by one ear, and put him into the Boy's arms.

That night, and for many nights after, the Velveteen Rabbit slept in the Boy's bed. At first he found it rather uncomfortable, for the Boy hugged him very tight, and sometimes he rolled over on him, and sometimes he pushed him so far under the pillow that the Rabbit could scarcely breathe. And he missed, too, those long moonlight hours in the nursery, when all the house was silent, and his talks with the Skin Horse. But very soon he grew to like it, for the Boy used to talk to him, and made nice tunnels for him, under the bedclothes, that he said were like the burrows the real rabbits lived in. And they had splendid games together, in whispers, when Nana had gone away to her supper and left the night light burning on the mantelpiece. And when the Boy dropped off to sleep, the Rabbit would snuggle down close under his little warm chin and dream, with the Boy's hands clasped close round him all night long.

And so time went on, and the little Rabbit was very happy—so happy that he never noticed how his beautiful velveteen fur was getting shabbier and shabbier, and his tail coming unsewn, and all the pink rubbed off his nose where the Boy had kissed him.

Spring came, and they had long days in the garden, for wherever the Boy went the Rabbit went too. He had rides in the wheelbarrow, and picnics on the grass, and lovely fairy huts built for him under the raspberry canes behind the flower border. And once, when the Boy was called away suddenly to go out to tea, the Rabbit was left out on the lawn until long after dusk, and Nana had to come and look for him with the candle because the Boy couldn't go to sleep unless he was there. He was wet through with the dew and quite earthy from diving into the burrows the Boy had made for him in the flower bed, and Nana grumbled as she rubbed him off with a corner of her apron.

"You must have your old Bunny!" she said. "Fancy all that fuss for a toy!"

The Boy sat up in bed and stretched out his hands.

"Give me my Bunny!" he said. "You mustn't say that. He isn't a toy. He's REAL!"

When the little Rabbit heard that he was happy, for he knew that what the Skin Horse had said was true at last. The nursery magic had happened to him, and he was a toy no longer. He was Real. The Boy himself had said it.

That night he was almost too happy to sleep, and so much love stirred in his little sawdust heart that it almost burst. And into his boot-button eyes, that had long ago lost their polish, there came a look of wisdom and beauty, so that even Nana noticed it next morning when she picked him up, and said, "I declare if that old Bunny hasn't got quite a knowing expression!"

That was a wonderful Summer!

Near the house where they lived there was a wood, and in the long June evenings the Boy liked to go there after tea to play. He took the Velveteen Rabbit with him, and before he wandered off to pick flowers, or play at brigands among the trees, he always made the Rabbit a little nest somewhere among the bracken, where he would be quite cosy, for he was a kind-hearted little boy and he liked Bunny to be comfortable. One evening, while the Rabbit was lying there alone, watching the ants that ran to and fro between his velvet paws in the grass, he saw two strange beings creep out of the tall bracken near him.

They were rabbits like himself, but quite furry and brand-new. They must have been very well made, for their seams didn't show at all, and they changed shape in a queer way when they moved; one minute they were long and thin and the next minute fat and bunchy, instead of always staying the same like he did. Their feet padded softly on the ground, and they crept quite close to him, twitching their noses, while the Rabbit stared hard to see which side the clockwork stuck out, for he knew that people who jump generally have something to wind them up. But he couldn't see it. They were evidently a new kind of rabbit altogether.

They stared at him, and the little Rabbit stared back. And all the time their noses twitched.

"Why don't you get up and play with us?" one of them asked.

"I don't feel like it," said the Rabbit, for he didn't want to explain that he had no clockwork.

"Ho!" said the furry rabbit. "It's as easy as anything." And he gave a big hop sideways and stood on his hind legs.

"I don't believe you can!" he said.

"I can!" said the little Rabbit. "I can jump higher than anything!" He meant when the Boy threw him, but of course he didn't want to say so.

"Can you hop on your hind legs?" asked the furry rabbit.

That was a dreadful question, for the Velveteen Rabbit had no hind legs at all! The back of him was made all in one piece, like a pincushion. He sat still in the bracken, and hoped that the other rabbits wouldn't notice.

"I don't want to!" he said again.

But the wild rabbits have very sharp eyes. And this one stretched out his neck and looked.

"He hasn't got any hind legs!" he called out. "Fancy a rabbit without any hind legs!" And he began to laugh.

"I have!" cried the little Rabbit. "I have got hind legs! I am sitting on them!"

"Then stretch them out and show me, like this!" said the wild rabbit. And he began to whirl round and dance, till the little Rabbit got quite dizzy.

"I don't like dancing," he said. "I'd rather sit still!"

But all the while he was longing to dance, for a funny new tickly feeling ran through him, and he felt he would give anything in the world to be able to jump about like these rabbits did.

The strange rabbit stopped dancing, and came quite close. He came so close this time that his long whiskers brushed the Velveteen Rabbit's ear, and then he wrinkled his nose suddenly and flattened his ears and jumped backwards.

"He doesn't smell right!" he exclaimed. "He isn't a rabbit at all! He isn't real!"

"I *am* Real!" said the little Rabbit. "I am Real! The Boy said so!" And he nearly began to cry.

Just then there was a sound of footsteps, and the Boy ran past near them, and with a stamp of feet and a flash of white tails the two strange rabbits disappeared.

"Come back and play with me!" called the little Rabbit. "Oh, do come back! I *know* I am Real!"

But there was no answer, only the little ants ran to and fro, and the bracken swayed gently where the two strangers had passed. The Velveteen Rabbit was all alone.

"Oh, dear!" he thought. "Why did they run away like that? Why couldn't they stop and talk to me?"

For a long time he lay very still, watching the bracken, and hoping that they would come back. But they never returned, and presently the sun sank lower and the little white moths fluttered out, and the Boy came and carried him home.

Weeks passed, and the little Rabbit grew very old and shabby, but the Boy loved him just as much. He loved him so hard that he loved all his whiskers off, and the pink lining to his ears turned grey, and his brown spots faded. He even began to lose his shape, and he scarcely looked like a rabbit any more, except to the Boy. To him he was always beautiful, and that was all that the little Rabbit cared about. He didn't mind how he looked to other people, because the nursery magic had made him Real, and when you are Real shabbiness doesn't matter.

And then, one day, the Boy was ill.

His face grew very flushed, and he talked in his sleep, and his little body was so hot that it burned the Rabbit when he held him close. Strange people came and went in the nursery, and a light burned all night, and through it all the little Velveteen Rabbit lay there, hidden from sight under the bedclothes, and he never stirred, for he was afraid that if they found him someone might take him away, and he knew that the Boy needed him.

It was a long weary time, for the Boy was too ill to play, and the little Rabbit found it rather dull with nothing to do all day long. But he snuggled down patiently, and looked forward to the time when the Boy should be well again, and they would go out in the garden amongst the flowers and the butterflies and play splendid games in the raspberry thicket like they used to. All sorts of delightful things he planned, and while the Boy lay half asleep he crept up close to the pillow and whispered them in his ear. And presently the fever turned, and the Boy got better. He was able to sit up in bed and look at picture books, while the little Rabbit cuddled close at his side. And one day, they let him get up and dress.

It was a bright, sunny morning, and the windows stood wide open. They had carried the Boy out on to the balcony, wrapped in a shawl, and the little Rabbit lay tangled up among the bedclothes, thinking.

The Boy was going to the seaside tomorrow. Everything was arranged, and now it only remained to carry out the doctor's orders. They talked about it all, while the little Rabbit lay under the bedclothes, with just his head peeping out, and listened. The room was to be disinfected, and all the books and toys that the Boy had played with in bed must be burnt.

"Hurrah!" thought the little Rabbit. "Tomorrow we shall go to the seaside!" For the Boy had often talked of the seaside, and he wanted very much to see the big waves coming in, and the tiny crabs, and the sand castles.

Just then Nana caught sight of him.

"How about his old Bunny?" she asked.

"*That?*" said the doctor. "Why, it's a mass of scarlet fever germs! Burn it at once. What? Nonsense! Get him a new one. He mustn't have that any more!"

And so the little Rabbit was put into a sack with the old picture books and a lot of rubbish, and carried out to the end of the garden behind the fowl-house. That was a fine place to make a bonfire, only the gardener was too busy just then to attend to it. He had the potatoes to dig and the green peas to gather, but next morning he promised to come quite early and burn the whole lot.

That night the Boy slept in a different bedroom, and he had a new bunny to sleep with him. It was a splendid bunny, all white plush with real glass eyes, but the Boy was too excited to care very much about it. For tomorrow he was going to the seaside, and that in itself was such a wonderful thing that he could think of nothing else.

And while the Boy was asleep, dreaming of the seaside, the little Rabbit lay among the old picture books in the corner behind the fowl-house, and he felt very lonely. The sack had been left untied, and so by wriggling a bit he was able to get his head through the opening and look out. He was shivering a little, for he had always been used to sleeping in a proper bed, and by this time his coat had worn so thin and threadbare from hugging that it was no longer any protection to him. Nearby he could see the thicket of raspberry canes, growing tall and close like a tropical jungle, in whose shadow he had played with the Boy on bygone mornings. He thought of those long sunlit hours in the garden—how happy they were—and a great sadness came over him. He seemed to see them all pass before him, each more beautiful than the other, the fairy huts in the flower bed, the quiet evenings in the wood when he lay in the bracken and the little ants ran over his paws; the wonderful day when he first knew that he was Real. He thought of the Skin Horse, so wise and gentle, and all that he had told him. Of what use was it to be loved and lose one's beauty and become Real if it all ended like this? And a tear, a real tear, trickled down his little shabby velvet nose and fell to the ground.

And then a strange thing happened. For where the tear had fallen a flower grew out of the ground, a mysterious flower, not at all like any that grew in the garden. It had slender green leaves the colour of emeralds, and in the centre of the leaves a blossom like a golden cup. It was so beautiful that the little Rabbit forgot to cry, and just lay there watching it. And presently the blossom opened, and out of it there stepped a fairy.

She was quite the loveliest fairy in the whole world. Her dress was of pearl and dewdrops, and there were flowers round her neck and in her hair, and her face was like the most perfect flower of all. And she came close to the little Rabbit and gathered him up in her arms and kissed him on his velveteen nose that was all damp from crying.

"Little Rabbit," she said, "don't you know who I am?"

The Rabbit looked up at her, and it seemed to him that he had seen her face before, but he couldn't think where.

"I am the nursery magic Fairy," she said. "I take care of all the playthings that the children have loved. When they are old and worn out and the children don't need them any more, then I come and take them away with me and turn them into Real."

"Wasn't I Real before?" asked the little Rabbit.

"You were Real to the Boy," the Fairy said, "because he loved you. Now you shall be Real to everyone."

And she held the little Rabbit close in her arms and flew with him into the wood.

It was light now, for the moon had risen. All the forest was beautiful, and the fronds of the bracken shone like

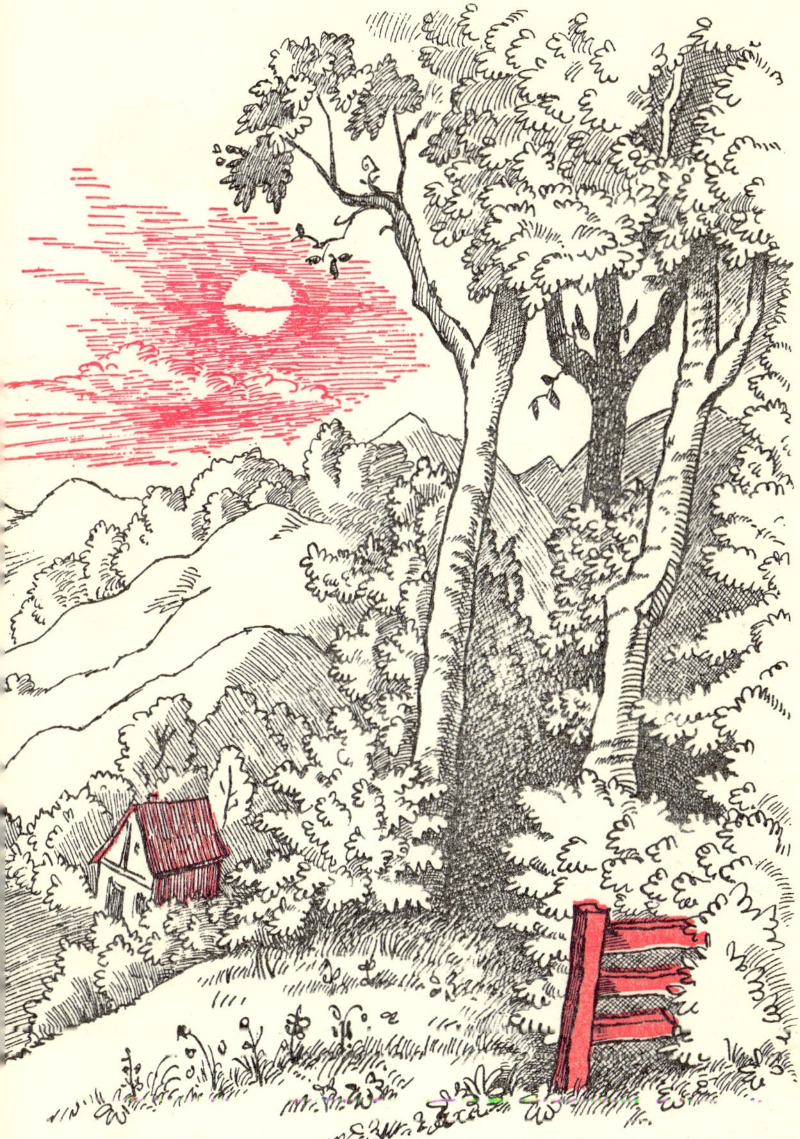

frosted silver. In the open glade between the tree trunks the wild rabbits danced with their shadows on the velvet grass, but when they saw the Fairy they all stopped dancing and stood round in a ring to stare at her.

"I've brought you a new playfellow," the Fairy said. "You must be very kind to him and teach him all he needs to know in Rabbitland, for he is going to live with you for ever and ever!"

And she kissed the little Rabbit again and put him down on the grass.

"Run and play, little Rabbit!" she said.

But the little Rabbit sat quite still for a moment and never moved. For when he saw all the wild rabbits dancing around him he suddenly remembered about his hind legs, and he didn't want them to see that he was made all in one piece. He did not know that when the Fairy kissed him that last time she had changed him altogether. And he might have sat there a long time, too shy to move, if just then something hadn't tickled his nose, and before he thought what he was doing he lifted his hind toe to scratch it.

And he found that he actually had hind legs! Instead of dingy velveteen he had brown fur, soft and shiny, his ears twitched by themselves, and his whiskers were so long that they brushed the grass. He gave one leap and the joy of using those hind legs was so great that he went springing about the turf on them, jumping sideways and whirling round as the others did, and he grew so excited that when at last he did stop to look for the Fairy she had gone.

He was a Real Rabbit at last, at home with the other rabbits.

Autumn passed and Winter, and in the Spring, when the days grew warm and sunny, the Boy went out to play in the wood behind the house. And while he was playing, two rabbits crept out from the bracken and peeped at him. One of them was brown all over, but the other had strange markings under his fur, as though long ago he had been spotted, and the spots still showed through. And about his little soft nose and his round black eyes there was something familiar, so that the Boy thought to himself:

"Why, he looks just like my old Bunny that was lost when I had scarlet fever!"

But he never knew that it really was his own Bunny, come back to look at the child who had first helped him to be Real.

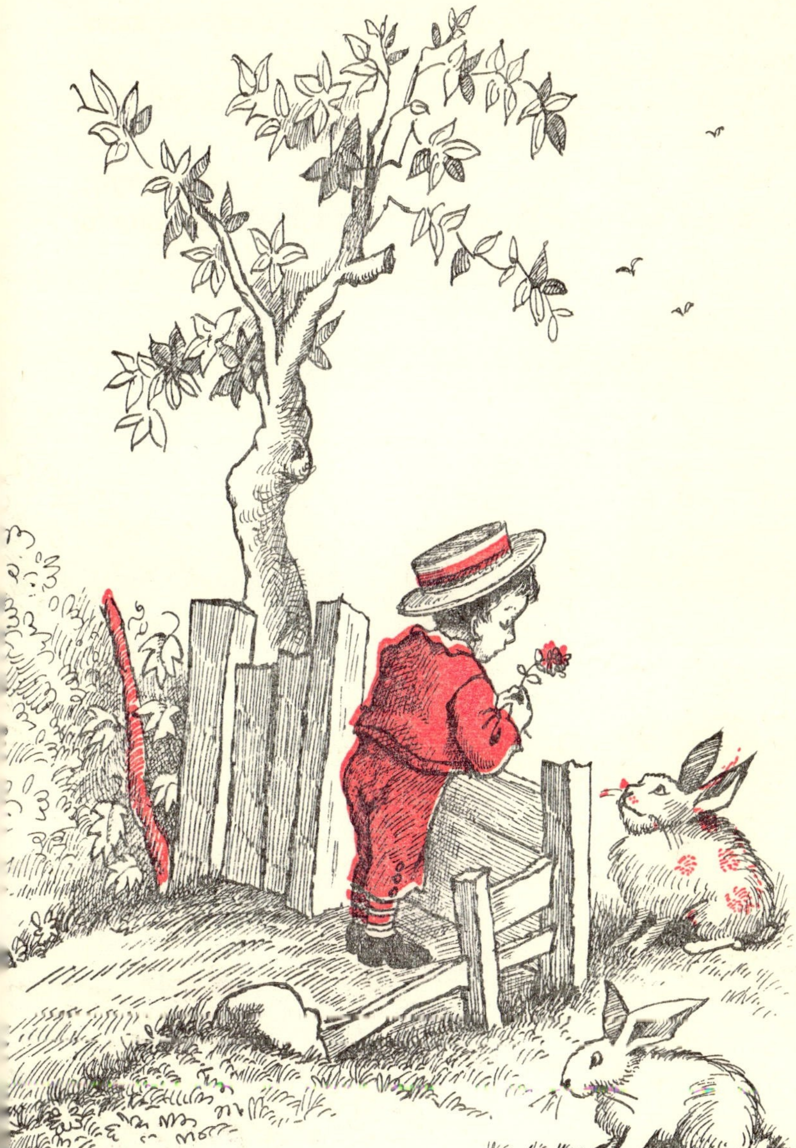

Simple Sewing: A Doll and Her Clothes

by TINA LEE

illustrated by LUCIANA ROSELLI

Text from *What To Do Now*, copyright, 1946, by Tina Lee, and published by Doubleday & Company, Inc.

STOCKING DOLLS

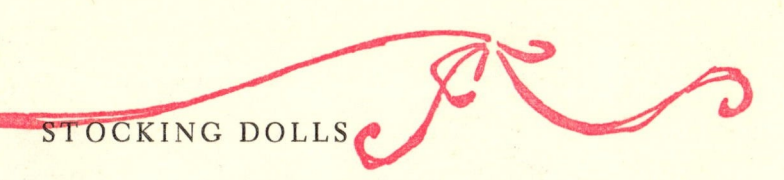

Turn an old stocking inside out, press it with a warm iron, and mark off on the stocking with a soft pencil as shown in Picture 1 on page 108. Mark off two pieces like Picture 2 for arms. Run a row of fine machine stitching on pencil marks. Trim off extra material. Turn to right side and stuff with cotton. Gather tightly together at open top. Tie darning cotton around waist and neck. Stuff arm pieces and sew to doll's shoulders. Use black cloth circles for eyes and a piece of red cloth for mouth. The hair is made from black fringe or yarn. Or you can make a bunny exactly like the doll. Use a pair of stiff paper ears cut as shown in Picture 3. Add thread whiskers and a cotton tail.

STOCKING DOLLS

Picture 1 — 4½", 10½", 4", 1½"
Picture 2 — 4½", 1½"
Picture 3 — 5", 2½"

Picture 4 — 2½", ¾", 7¼", 4½", ½", ¼"

Picture 5

Gather neck to fit doll

Hem armholes

Clip seam here

Begin at bottom and sew up side seams for 4¾"

Clip seam here

Turn ½" hem in bottom of skirt

KIMONO DRESS

The clothes on these pages were designed to fit a 12-inch doll. They will all fit the stocking doll. If you want to make these designs for a larger or a smaller doll, change the measurements according to her size. These designs are all easy to make. Follow directions carefully. Do not try to hurry and your doll clothes will be successful.

KIMONO DRESS

Kimono style means that the sleeves are cut in one piece with the dress. This is the easiest way to make doll clothes.

Start with a piece of paper which measures 9 inches by 7¼ inches. Fold in half to measure 4½ inches by 7¼ inches. Mark off as shown in Picture 4. Cut on pencil lines. This is your pattern. Fold your fabric double and be sure it is well pressed before you cut. Pin your pattern to your double fabric and cut around the pattern. You will have two pieces. One is the back, the other the front. Sew them together as shown in Picture 5. Hem armholes and bottom. Cut 3-inch slash in center back for a placket. Gather neck to fit doll. Sew small snap at top of placket and tie a narrow ribbon around the waist.

CIRCLE HAT

This is a very jolly hat. Make it from thin felt, a straw circle, or piqué. After you have made one for your doll, try one for yourself. Of course you will have to start with a larger circle. For your doll, use an 8½-inch circle. Fold in half as in Picture 6 on page 112. Now fold as indicated by dotted lines in Picture 7. Gather one thickness of the material between folded edges. See Picture 8. Tie with yarn or ribbon bow. Open hat. Trim with feather or flower.

MEXICAN BLOUSE

When on your doll, this blouse gathers softly around the neck and is very pretty. To make the pattern, start with a paper which measures 9½ inches by 7 inches. Fold in half to measure 4¾ inches by 7 inches. Mark out as indicated in Picture 9. Cut out on pencil marks. Pin this pattern to a double thickness of the fabric and cut carefully. Sew pieces together as indicated in Picture 10. Gather around the neck with big stitches of colored yarn.

JUMPER SKIRT

Fold in half a paper which measures 8 inches by 4½ inches to measure 4 inches by 4½ inches. Mark out as shown in Picture 11. Open pattern and pin to a double piece of fabric. Sew as shown in Picture 12, leaving 1¾ inches open on one seam for a placket. Turn front side of placket in, leave back part as an extension. Press seams open. Hem top and bottom of skirt. Sew a snap on the placket. Cut two straps 6 inches long by 1 inch wide. Turn in ¼ inch on both sides and stitch down. Attach these straps to skirt, using small buttons to hold them in place.

CIRCLE HAT

← 8½" →

picture 6

picture 7

folded hat

picture 8

MEXICAN BLOUSE

folded edge
Picture 9

← 5¼" →

sew hem neck and armhole sew

Picture 10

Sew side seams

hem

JUMPER SKIRT

Picture 11

← 4 →

Picture 12

Turn hem at waist

← Sew side seams

turn ½" hem

APRON

← 1¼ inch square

9½

4½

25"

1½

Picture 13

← 5¾" →

Picture 14

DIRNDL

Picture 15

POINTED BAG

Picture 16 Picture 17

Picture 18

APRON

These directions are for a very simple apron which can be made quickly and easily.

Cut three pieces of material the sizes shown on the charts. One piece forms the apron, the small square is for the pocket, and the long narrow one forms the waistband and apron string. Sew pocket to apron as shown in Picture 13 on page 113. Be sure to leave top free. Fold long band in half to measure ¾ of an inch wide. Gather center of apron at top, making it measure 5¾ inches. Slip it between the folded band as shown in Picture 14. Hold firmly in place by making two rows of fine stitches.

You can make many different aprons by using this pattern. A lace apron made this way is very pretty, especially if you use a ribbon for the waistband and strings. Your doll can have a nurse's apron if you will make two shoulder straps about ½ inch wide and 10 inches long and sew them to the center of the waistband in front.

DIRNDL

Cut a piece of cloth 5½ inches by 20 inches. Seam ends together for 3½ inches, leaving a 2-inch placket. See Picture 15. Press seam open. Put a ½-inch hem in the bottom of skirt. Make a band 2 inches wide and long enough to fit around your doll's waist. Fold this band in half to measure 1 inch wide. Gather skirt to size of band and sew them together as shown.

POINTED BAG

This bag can be made for yourself or your dolls. For this pointed bag, start with a 12-inch square of felt or other fabric that does not need hemming. Fold your square and stitch each seam together for 3½ inches from the point as shown in Picture 16. Sew a ring or make a thread loop at each point marked with black dot in Picture 17. Run one cord through these rings as indicated by black string and a second one as indicated by white string in Picture 18.

Let's Look at Russia

by GLADYS SCHWARCZ

with drawings by EARL THOLLANDER

The letters U.S.S.R. stand for a long name and a very large country, the Union of Soviet Socialist Republics. Before 1917, this huge country was called simply Russia. It is still more widely known by this name today.

Russia is almost three times the size of the United States. It stretches halfway around the world, far into the continents of both Europe and Asia. The European part consists of a long, flat to gently rolling plain, crossed by the Ural Mountains and a number of rivers. In Asian Russia, there are the cold, dry tundras of northern Siberia, with forests, high mountains and plateaus lying to the south.

Statue of Peter the Great

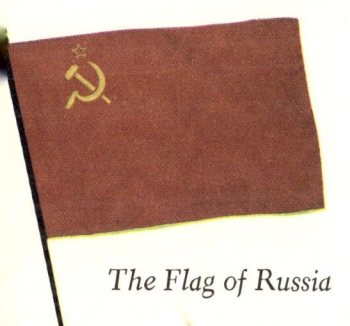

The Flag of Russia

The weather in Russia is generally cold. The rainfall is not very heavy, and there are frequent dry spells.

Within this big land live about 200,000,000 people. They are the direct descendants of the tribes which dwelt in western Russia over 1100 years ago. For almost three centuries they were ruled by the powerful Tartars from Asia.

View of the Moscow skyline with Lenin Stadium at the right

Fountain of the Republics

About the time that America was discovered, Ivan III challenged the Tartars and declared Russian independence. Some 200 years later, Peter the Great, an emperor, or tsar, of unusual ability, extended Russia's borders to the Baltic and Black Seas, establishing seaports for trade with Europe.

Russia was still an industrially backward nation as late as 1900, despite its size and natural resources. Military defeats by Japan and during World War I, and a terrible famine within its borders, created great unrest among the people. Soon there was rebellion and fighting.

In 1917, Tsar Nicholas II gave up his throne. Months

Army men walk in the Kremlin.

Enormous "Tsar's Bell"

later, the Communists, a small group of workers and soldiers in St. Petersburg and Moscow, seized control of the government. The Communists, or Soviets, believed in a state in which the government, land, and machinery were supposed to be controlled by the workers. In reality, Russia has been ruled by a few top men, Lenin, Stalin, and Khrushchev, and the people have been denied many personal freedoms.

The heart of Russia is in its capital city, Moscow. At Moscow's center stands the Kremlin, a walled-in section which encloses beautiful old cathedrals, the palaces of for-

St. Nicholas Cathedral

ARCTI
GERMANY
DENMARK
NORWAY
SWEDEN
GULF of BOTHNIA
FINLAND
BARENTS SEA
MURMANSK
LENINGRAD
ARKHANGEL'SK
2
MINSK
ODESSA
KIEV
NAR'YAN-MAR
11
DNEPROPETROVSK
9
MOSCOW
URAL MTS.
R.
ROSTOV
STALINGRAD
KUYBYSHEV
VOLGA
BLACK SEA
CAUCASUS MTS.
5
OB R.
BATUMI
MAGNITOGORSK
CASPIAN SEA
BAKU
12
ARAL SEA
OMSK
8
7
ASHKHABAD
TASHKENT
IRAN
3
L. BALKHASH
OSH
Robert J. Lee
AFGHANISTAN
INDIA
C
H

Can you find the following things on this map? **1.** Brown bear **2.** Ukranian musician playing bandura **3.** Sturgeon, source of caviar **4.** Asiatic Russian **5.** Women sacking grain **6.** Askanianova ram **7.** Peasant farmer **8.** Industrial factory **9.** Bell tower of Ivan the Great **10.** Typical Russian architecture **11.** Steel-mill worker **12.** Prize steer **13.** Tiger **14.** Dancers

Apartments in Rostov-on-Don   *A busy main street in Kiev*

mer tsars, and museums containing priceless objects from the royal courts, including the world's largest bell, the "Tsar's Bell." Here too are the Soviet government offices.

St. Petersburg, the handsome city founded by Peter the Great, has been renamed Leningrad in Lenin's honor. Russians flock to Leningrad to see St. Nicholas Cathedral and the luxurious Peterhof Palace, fine examples of the European art and architecture Tsar Peter introduced to Russia.

Agriculture is the mainstay of Russia. The Ukraine, a section in the southernmost part of European Russia, is the breadbasket of the country. The rich black soil and fertile fields around Kiev and Kharkov supply the nation's wheat, rye, corn, sugarbeets, and potatoes.

Great fountain and statues in Peterhof Palace, Leningrad

Large, typical collective farm near Kharkov in the Ukraine

In Russia a farmer does not own the land on which he works. All of the land is owned and managed by collective farms and state farms. The farmers grow the crops, giving the state the biggest part of their produce. They receive their share from what is left. In recent years, Russian agricultural production has risen to a high peak.

Besides agriculture, the Ukraine is a large center for mining and industry. In Rostov-on-Don, new apartment buildings like those in the United States have been erected to house the large numbers of industrial workers.

In Russia women can be seen doing many hard, physical jobs, because there is a shortage of manpower.

Through the port of Odessa on the Black Sea move

Women laborers in Leningrad   Fontana Beach on Black Sea

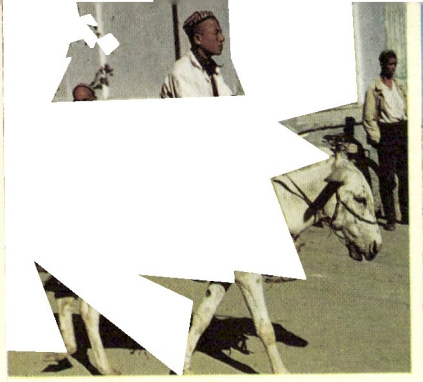

A street in Central Asia   Asian farmers in Moscow

many of the products Russia sells to southern Europe and Asia. The warm weather in this region brings vacationers from the big industrial cities to Fontana Beach and other seaside resorts along the Black Sea and Crimean Peninsula.

Soviet Central Asia lies east of the Caspian Sea. It is a very large territory once ruled by wandering desert tribes and farmers of the fertile valleys. Cotton is the king of crops here. The land is rich in copper, lead, coal, zinc, uranium, and other metals and minerals.

The people of Central Asia are of many nationalities. Almost all of them are Moslems, though some of the Moslem commandments are no longer obeyed. Women have stopped wearing the veil. But the men still wear tiny skullcaps.

Russia is a very sports-conscious country. Men and women train carefully to compete in such popular sport-

"Spartakiad" athletes train.   Children in a Moscow school ing events as the "Spartakiad." At recent Olympic games, Russian athletes have won many honors.

Just as in the United States, all children must go to school in Russia. One of the outstanding accomplishments of the Communist government is the almost complete elimination of illiteracy. Though the publication of books and magazines is controlled by the government, there is a wide variety of reading material available.

The Russian alphabet is the Cyrillic rather than the Latin alphabet used by the western world. This difference in writing has tended to cut Russia off from much of European culture and literature. Yet Russian books, plays, music, and her fine ballet are world famous.

Cold, icy Siberia is considered a land with a bright future. It is reported to possess unlimited resources in land, forests, metals, and minerals, yet to be developed.

Several months after Germany invaded Russia in 1941, the United States and Russia became allies. But as soon as the war ended, friendly relations between the two nations became strained, changing into what has been termed "the cold war." This tension grew because Russia was establishing Communist governments in the lands she had occupied during the war. The United States wanted these nations to choose their own manner of government by conducting free elections.

Postwar Russia has grown tremendously in industrial, scientific, and military strength. Whether the world will have peace or war and survive nuclear destruction depends largely on future relations between the U.S.S.R. and the non-Communist nations.

A *Japanese Fairy Tale*
The Wonderful Teakettle

illustrated by EIICHI MITSUI

A long, long time ago, at the temple of Morinji, in the province of Kotsuke, there lived an old priest.

This old priest was very fond of the ceremonial preparing and drinking of tea known as *Chanoyu*; indeed, it was his chief interest and pleasure in life to conduct this ceremony.

One day he chanced to find in a second-hand shop a very nice-looking old Teakettle, which he bought and took home with him, highly pleased by its fine shape and artistic appearance.

Next day he brought out his new purchase, and sat for a long time turning it round on this side and on that, and admiring it.

"You are a regular beauty, that's what you are," he said. "I shall invite all my friends to the *Chanoyu*, and how astonished they will be at finding such an exquisite kettle as this!"

He placed his treasure on top of a box where he could see it to the best advantage, and sat admiring it and planning how he should invite his guests. After a while he became drowsy and began to nod, and at last fell forward, his head on his desk, fast asleep.

Then a wonderful transformation took place. The Teakettle began to move. From its spout appeared a hairy head; at the other side out came a fine bushy tail; next, four feet made themselves visible; while fine fur seemed gradually to cover the surface of the kettle. At last, jumping off the box, it began capering about the room for all the world just like a badger.

Three young novices, pupils of the priest, who were at study in the next room, heard the noise; and, when one of them peeped through the sliding doors, what was his astonishment to see the Teakettle on four feet dancing up and down the room!

He cried out: "Oh! What a wonderful thing! The Teakettle is changed into a badger!"

"What!" said the second novice. "Do you mean to say that the Teakettle is turned into a badger? What nonsense!" So saying, he pushed his companion to one side and peeped in, but he was terrified by what he saw, and screamed: "It's a goblin! It's coming at us; let us run away!"

The third novice was not so easily frightened.

"Come, this is rather fun," said he. "How the creature does jump, to be sure! I will rouse the master, and let him see, too."

So he went into the room and shook the priest, crying: "Wake! Master, wake! A strange thing has happened."

"What's the matter?" said the old man, drowsily rubbing his eyes. "What a noisy fellow you are!"

"Anyone would be noisy when such a strange thing as this is going on," said the novice. "Only look, master, your Teakettle has got feet, and is running about."

"What! What! What! What's that you say?" asked the priest again. "The kettle got feet! What's this! Let me see!"

But by the time the old man was thoroughly roused, the Teakettle had turned into its ordinary shape, and stood quietly on its box again.

"What foolish young fellows you are!" said the priest. "There stands a kettle on top of a box; surely there is nothing very strange in that. No, no, I have heard of the rolling pin that grew a pair of wings and flew away, but, long as I have lived, never have I heard before of a teakettle walking about on its own feet. You will never make me believe that."

But for all that, the priest was a little uneasy in his mind, and kept thinking of the incident all that day. When evening came, and he was alone in his room, he took down the kettle, filled it with water, and set it upon the embers to boil, intending to make some tea. But, as soon as the water began to boil, "Hot! Hot!" cried the kettle, and jumped off the fire.

"Help! Help!" cried the priest, terrified out of his wits.

But when the novices rushed to his help, the kettle at once resumed its natural form; so one of them, seizing a stick, cried, "We'll soon find out whether it's alive or not," and began beating it with might and main. There was evidently no life in the thing, and only a metallic clang! clang! responded to his lusty blows.

Then the old priest heartily repented having bought the mischievous Teakettle, and was debating in his own mind how he should get rid of it, when who should drop in but the tinker!

"Here's the very man," thought the priest. A bargain was soon struck; the tinker bought the Teakettle for a few coppers, and carried it home, well pleased with his purchase.

Before going to bed he took another look at it, and found it still better than he had at first thought, so he went to sleep that night in the best of spirits.

In the midst of a pleasant dream the tinker suddenly started up, thinking he heard somebody moving in the room, but, when he opened his eyes and looked about, he could see nobody.

"It was only a dream, I suppose," said he to himself as he turned over and went to sleep again.

But he was disturbed once more by someone calling: "Tinker! Tinker! Get up! Get up!"

This time he sprang up, wide awake, and lo and behold! There was the Teakettle, with the head, tail, feet, and fur of a badger, strutting up and down the room!

"Goblin! Goblin!" shrieked the tinker.

But the Teakettle laughed and said: "Don't be frightened, my dear tinker. I am not a goblin, only a wonderful teakettle. My name is *Bumbuku-Chagama*, and I will bring good luck to anyone who treats me well; but, of course, I don't like to be set on the fire, and then beaten with sticks, as happened to me up at the temple yesterday."

"How can I please you, then?" asked the tinker. "Shall I keep you in a box?"

"Oh! No, no!" answered the Teakettle. "I like nice sweet things to eat, and sometimes a little wine to drink, just like yourself. Will you keep me in your house and feed me? And, as I would not be a burden upon you, I will work for you in any way you like."

To this the tinker agreed.

Next morning he provided a good feast for *Bumbuku*, who then spoke:

"I certainly am a wonderful and accomplished Teakettle, and my advice is that you take me round the country as a show, with accompaniments of singing and music."

The tinker, thinking well of this advice, at once started a show, which he named the *Bumbuku-Chagama*. The lucky Teakettle at once made the affair a success, for not only did he walk about on four legs, but he danced the tightrope, and went through all kinds of acrobatic performances, ending by making a profound bow to the spectators, and begging for their future patronage.

The fame of these performances soon spread abroad, and the theater was filled daily to overflowing until, at length, even the princes of the land sent to order the tinker and his kettle to come to them, and the show would take place, to the great delight of the princesses and ladies of the court.

At last the tinker grew so rich that he retired from business, and, wishing his faithful kettle also to be at rest, he took it back, together with a large share of his wealth, to the temple of Morinji, where it was laid up as a precious treasure and, some say, even worshipped as a saint.

Beezus and Her Imagination

by BEVERLY CLEARY

illustrated by MIRCEA VASILIU

Beatrice Quimby's biggest problem was her little sister Ramona. Beatrice, or Beezus (as everyone called her, because that was what Ramona had called her when she first learned to talk), knew other nine-year-old girls who had little sisters who went to nursery school, but she did not know anyone with a little sister like Ramona.

Beezus felt that the biggest trouble with four-year-old Ramona was that she was just plain exasperating. If Ramona drank lemonade through a straw, she blew into the straw as hard as she could to see what would happen. If she played with her finger paints in the front yard, she wiped

Text from *Beezus and Ramona*, copyright ©, 1955, by Beverly Cleary, and published by William Morrow & Company.

her hands on the neighbors' cat. That was the exasperating sort of thing Ramona did.

Beezus and Ramona both looked forward to Friday afternoons after school—Beezus because she attended the art class in the recreation center in Glenwood Park, Ramona because she was allowed to go to the park with Beezus and play in the sand pile until the class was over. This Friday, while Beezus held Ramona by the hand and waited for the traffic light to change from red to green, she thought how wonderful it would be to have an imagination like Ramona's.

"Oh, you know Ramona. Her imagination runs away with her," Mother said, when Ramona made up a story about seeing a fire engine crash into a garbage truck.

"That child has an imagination a mile long," the Quimbys' grown-up friends remarked when Ramona sat in the middle of the living-room floor in a plastic wading pool she had dragged up from the basement and pretended she was in a boat in the middle of a lake.

"Did you ever see so much imagination in such a little girl?" the neighbors asked one another when Ramona hopped around the yard pretending she was the Easter bunny.

One spring day Ramona had got lost, because she started out to find the pot of gold at the end of the rainbow. The rainbow had appeared to end in the park until she reached the park, but then it looked as if it ended behind the Supermarket. When the police brought Ramona home, Father said, "Sometimes I think Ramona has too much imagination."

Nobody, reflected Beezus, ever says anything about my imagination. Nobody at all. And she wished, more than anything, that she had imagination. How pleased Miss Robbins, the art teacher, would be with her if she had an imagination like Ramona's!

Unfortunately, Beezus was not very good at painting—at least not the way Miss Robbins wanted boys and girls to paint. She wanted them to use their imagination and to feel free. Beezus still squirmed with embarrassment when she thought of her first painting, a picture of a dog with *bowwow* coming out of his mouth in a balloon. Miss Robbins pointed out that only in the funny papers did dogs have *bowwow* coming out of their mouths in balloons. *Bowwow* in a balloon was not art. When Miss Robbins did think one of Beezus' paintings was good enough to put up on the wall, she always tacked it way down at the end, never in the center. Beezus wished she could have a painting in the center of the wall.

"Hurry up, Ramona," Beezus coaxed. Then she noticed that her sister was dragging a string along behind her. "Oh, Ramona," she protested, "why did you have to bring Ralph with you?" Ralph was an imaginary green lizard Ramona liked to pretend she was leading by a string.

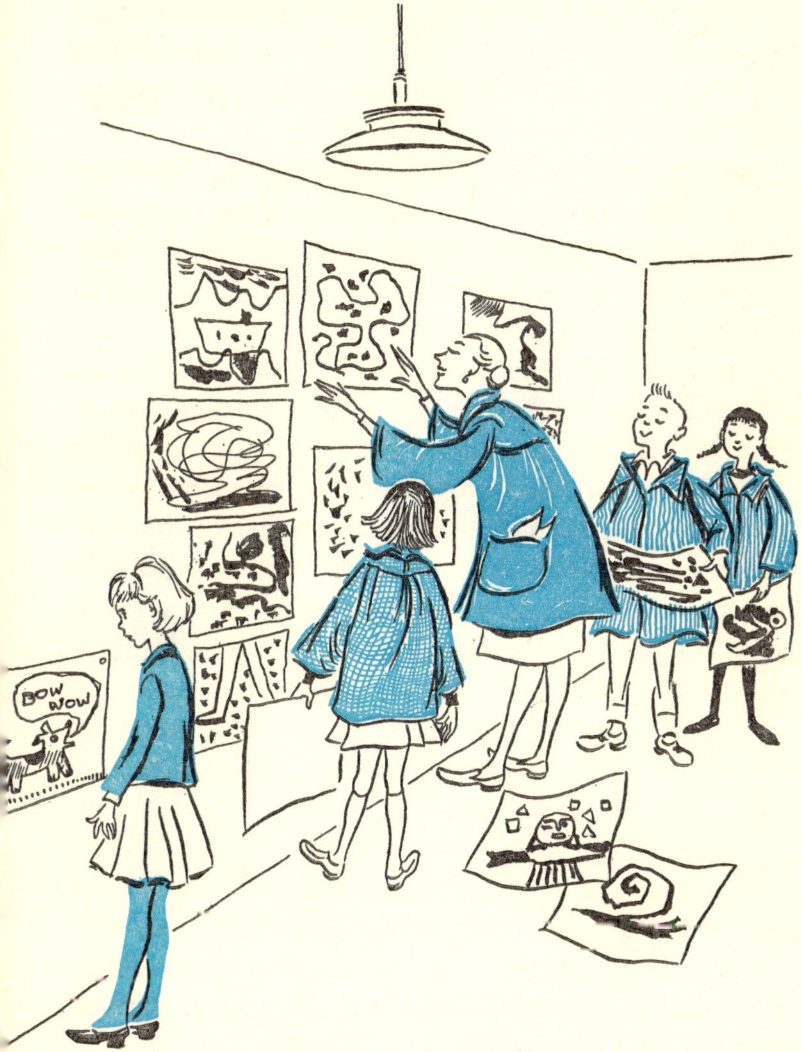
BOW WOW

"I love Ralph," said Ramona firmly, "and Ralph likes to go to the park."

Beezus knew it was easier to pretend along with Ramona than to try to make her stop. Anyway, it was better to have her pretend to lead a lizard than to pretend to be a lizard herself. "Can't you carry him?" she suggested.

"No," said Ramona. "He's slimy."

When the girls came to the shopping district, Ramona had to stop at the drugstore scales and pretend to weigh herself while Beezus held Ralph's string. "I weigh fifty-eleven pounds," she announced, while Beezus smiled at Ramona's idea of her weight. It just goes to show how much imagination Ramona has, she thought.

At the radio-and-phonograph store Ramona insisted on petting His Master's Voice, the black-and-white plaster dog, bigger than Ramona, that always sat with one ear cocked in front of the door. Beezus thought admiringly about the amount of imagination it took to pretend that a scarred and chipped plaster dog was real. If only she had an imagination like Ramona's, maybe Miss Robbins would say her paintings were free and imaginative and would tack them on the middle of the wall.

When they reached the park, Beezus left Ramona and Ralph at the sand pile and, feeling more and more discouraged at her own lack of imagination, hurried to the recreation center. The class had already poured paints into their muffin tins and were painting on paper thumbtacked to drawing boards. The room hummed with activity. Miss Robbins, wearing a gay paint-smeared smock, flew from one artist to another, praising, correcting, suggesting.

Beezus waited until Miss Robbins finished explaining to a boy that he should not outline a mouth with black paint. Her mouth wasn't outlined in black, was it? Then Beezus said, "I'm sorry I'm late, Miss Robbins." She stared in fascination at Miss Robbins' earrings. They came almost to her shoulders and were made of silver wire twisted and bent into interesting shapes—not the shape of anything in particular, just interesting shapes.

"That's all right." Miss Robbins, her earrings swinging, smiled at Beezus. "Get your paints and paper. Today everyone is painting an imaginary animal."

"An imaginary animal?" Beezus repeated blankly. How could she possibly think of an imaginary animal? As Beezus

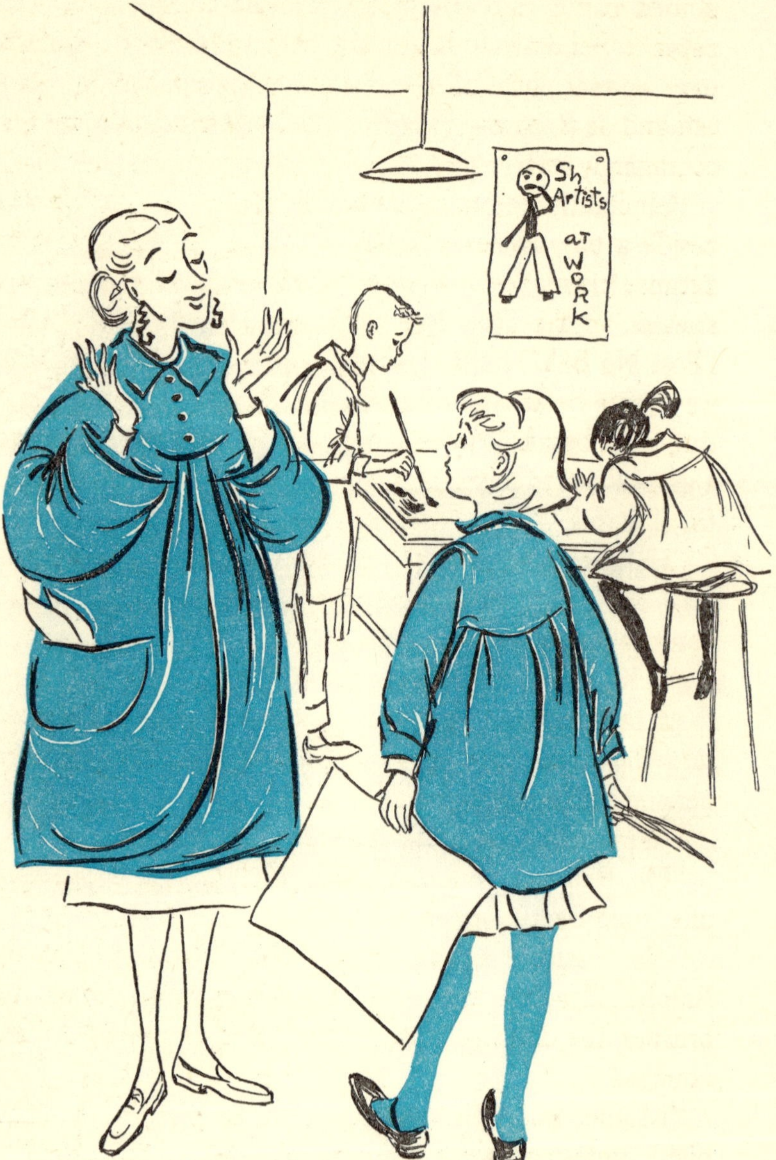
Sh
Artists
at
WORK

poured paints into her muffin tin and tacked a sheet of paper to her drawing board, she tried to think of an imaginary animal, but all the animals she could think of—cats and dogs, cows and horses, lions and giraffes—were discouragingly real.

Reluctantly Beezus took the only vacant seat, which was beside a boy named Wayne who came to the class only because his mother made him. Once Beezus had hung her sweater on the back of a chair, and Wayne had printed "Post No Bills" on it in chalk. Beezus had worn it all the way home before she discovered it. Since then she did not care to sit beside Wayne. Today she noticed he had parked a grape-flavored lollipop on a paper towel beside his muffin tin of paints.

"Hi, Beez," he greeted her. "No fair licking my sucker."

"I don't want your old sucker," answered Beezus. "And don't call me Beez."

"O.K., Beez," said Wayne.

At that moment the door opened and Ramona walked into the room. She was still dragging the string behind her and she looked angry.

"Why, hello," said Miss Robbins pleasantly.

"Oh, Ramona, you're supposed to be playing in the sand pile," said Beezus, going over to her.

"No," said Ramona flatly. "Howie threw sand on Ralph." Her dark eyes were busy taking in the paints, the brushes, the drawing boards. "I'm going to paint," she announced.

"Mother said you were supposed to play in the sand pile," protested Beezus. "You're too little for this class."

"You say that about everything," complained Ramona. Then she turned to Miss Robbins. "Don't step on Ralph," she said.

"Ralph is a make-believe green lizard she pretends she leads around on a string." Beezus was embarrassed at having to explain such a silly thing.

Miss Robbins laughed. "Well, here is a little girl with lots of imagination. How would you like to paint a picture of Ralph for us, Ramona?"

Beezus could not help feeling annoyed. Miss Robbins was letting Ramona stay in the class—the one place where she was never allowed to tag along! Miss Robbins would probably like her painting, because it would be so full of imagination. Ramona's pictures, in fact, were so full of imagination that it took even more imagination to tell what they were.

Ramona beamed at Miss Robbins, who found a drawing board for her and a stool, which she placed between Beezus and Wayne. She lifted Ramona onto the stool. "There. Now you can share your sister's paints," she said.

Ramona looked impressed at being allowed to paint with such big boys and girls. She sat quietly on her stool, watching everything around her.

Maybe she'll behave herself after all, thought Beezus as she dipped her brush into blue paint, and now I don't have to sit next to Wayne. Since Beezus still had not thought of an imaginary animal, she decided to start with the sky.

"Do the sky first," Beezus whispered to Ramona, who looked as if she did not know how to begin. Then Beezus faced her own work, determined to be free and imaginative. To be free on a piece of paper was not as easy as it sounded, she thought. Miss Robbins always said to start with the big areas of a picture and paint them bravely and boldly, so Beezus spread the sky on her paper with brave, bold strokes. Back and forth across the paper she swept her brush. Brave and bold and free—that was the way to do it.

Her sky turned out to be too wet, so while it dried a little, Beezus looked at what the other boys and girls were doing. Celia, who sat on her left, had already filled in a brave, bold background of pink, which she had sprinkled with big purple dots. Now she was painting a long gray line that wound all over her paper, in and out around the dots.

"What's that supposed to be?" whispered Beezus.

"I'm not sure yet," answered Celia.

Beezus felt better, because Celia was the kind of girl who usually knew exactly what she was doing and whose pictures were often tacked in the center of the wall. The boy on the other side of Celia, who always wanted to paint airplanes, was painting what looked like a giraffe made of pieces of machinery, and another boy was painting a thing that had two heads.

Beezus looked across Ramona to Wayne. He had not bothered with a sky at all. He had painted a hen. Beezus knew it was a hen, because he had printed in big letters, "This is a real hen," with an arrow pointing to it. Wayne always tried to do just the opposite of what Miss Robbins wanted.

"Hey, quit peeking," said Wayne in a loud voice.

"I'm not peeking," said Beezus, hastily trying to look as if she had been interested in Ramona's paper all the time.

Ramona had dipped her brush into blue paint and had painted a stripe across the top of her paper. "That's the sky," she said happily.

"But that's not the way the sky is." Beezus was trying to be helpful. She felt better, because Ramona had not plunged in and painted a picture full of imagination. "Skies should come farther down on the paper."

"The sky is up," said Ramona firmly.

Beezus decided she couldn't waste time explaining about skies, not when she still hadn't thought of an imaginary animal. Maybe she could take a real animal and sort of change it around. Let's see, she thought, I could take a horse and put feathers on it. No, all those feathers would be too hard to paint. Wings? That was it! A horse with wings was an imaginary animal—a real imaginary animal— because Mother had once read aloud a story about Pegasus, the winged horse, out of a library book. In the story Pegasus had been white, which was a real horse color. Beezus decided to be extra-imaginative. She would make her horse green—a green horse against a blue sky. Miss Robbins ought to like that. Beezus did not think blue and green looked very pretty together, but Miss Robbins often liked colors that Beezus thought did not really go together.

Beezus dipped her brush into green paint and outlined a wing against the sky. Next she outlined the body of the horse and a long tail that hung down. It was a magnificent horse. At least, Beezus hoped it would look magnificent when she finished it. Anyway, it was big, because Miss Robbins liked her artists to cover the whole paper. Quickly and neatly Beezus filled in the outline of the horse, because Miss Robbins, who was looking at Celia's picture, would look at hers next. Somehow the horse was not exactly what Beezus had in her mind's eye, but even so, compared to whatever Celia was painting, a green horse with wings was really a very good imaginary animal. And except for a couple of soggy places in the sky, her work was much neater than Celia's. Beezus waited for Miss Robbins to point this out.

Instead, Miss Robbins said, "Celia, your picture is work to be proud of. It is a difficult thing to get to be as free as this."

Then Miss Robbins moved on to Beezus, her long earrings swinging forward as she leaned over the drawing board. Beezus waited anxiously. Maybe her picture wasn't so good, after all. If Miss Robbins liked a gray line winding around a lot of purple dots, maybe she wouldn't like a flying horse. Maybe she liked things with no special shape, like those earrings.

"You have a good sky even if it is a little wet," said Miss Robbins.

Beezus was disappointed. Anybody could have a good sky.

Miss Robbins continued to study the picture. "Try to

think how a horse would look if it were really flying."

Beezus tried to think.

"What about the tail?" asked Miss Robbins. "Wouldn't the tail fly out behind instead of hanging down?"

"Especially is the wind blew real hard," said Wayne.

"Can't you make the horse look rounder?" asked Miss Robbins. "Think how a horse looks with the sun shining on him. Part of him would be in shadow."

"Not that horse," said Wayne. "She just copied it off a Mobilgas billboard, only she made it green instead of red."

"I did not!" said Beezus indignantly. Then she stared at her painting again. Now that Wayne pointed it out, she could see her horse did look like the one on the Mobilgas billboard at the service station where her father bought gasoline. He was a flat cardboard horse, not a magnificent horse at all. Her horse wasn't even as good as the horse on the billboard, because instead of a flying tail he had a tail that hung down like . . . well, like a mop.

"All right, Wayne," said Miss Robbins. "I'm sure Beezus did not mean to copy anything from a billboard."

"No, I didn't," said Beezus mournfully. "I was only trying to change a real animal around to make it imaginary, but I just don't have imagination, is all."

"Why, Beezus, of course you have imagination!" Miss Robbins sounded shocked at the idea of anyone's not having imagination.

"My little sister has lots of imagination," said Beezus. "Everybody says so."

Miss Robbins smiled reassuringly. "That doesn't mean that you don't have any. I think your trouble is that you work too hard. You don't have to be so neat. Why don't you start another painting and just try to have a good time with your paints?"

Beezus looked uncertain. It was a nice change to have a grownup tell her she didn't have to be neat, but she didn't understand how she could paint a good picture unless she worked at it. If only she had some imagination, like Ramona—but no, Miss Robbins said everybody had imagination. Well, if she had imagination, where was it? Why wasn't it helping her with her imaginary animal? All she could think of was the cardboard horse on the billboard.

Beezus glanced at Ramona, who had been surprisingly quiet for a long time, to see how she was coming along with her picture of Ralph. Except for the stripe of sky at the top, Ramona's paper was blank. Now she dipped her brush in yellow paint, divided the hairs of the brush into three tufts, and pressed them on the paper, leaving a mark like the track of a bird.

"That's not the way to use a paint brush," said Beezus. "Besides, you're getting paint on your fingers."

"Look—Ralph's feet marks," exclaimed Ramona, paying no attention to Beezus.

"You mean footprints," corrected Beezus. "Now go on and paint the rest of Ralph."

"Feet marks," said Ramona stubbornly, making more footprints across the paper. "And I can't paint him, because he's just pretend."

Oh, well, thought Beezus, maybe making footprints isn't good for the brush, but it keeps her quiet. She dabbled her own brush in green paint and tried to stir up her imagination. She felt a little encouraged because Ramona was having trouble too.

"Hey!" interrupted Wayne in a loud voice. "She's licking my sucker!"

"Ramona!" Beezus was horrified to see Ramona, no longer interested in footprints, calmly sucking Wayne's grape-flavored lollipop. "Ramona, put that down this instant! You're not supposed to lick other people's suckers."

"You give me that!" Wayne made a grab for his lollipop.

"No!" screamed Ramona, trying to hold it out of his reach. "I want it!"

"Ramona, give it to him," ordered Beezus. "It's all germy."

"You mean she's getting germs on it," said Wayne. "Give it to me!"

The rest of the class stopped painting to watch. Wayne made another grab for his lollipop. This time he grabbed Ramona by the wrist.

"Let go of her!" said Beezus angrily.

Ramona howled as Wayne tried to pry her fingers loose from the lollipop stick. He knocked against his muffin tin, which flipped into the air spattering paint over the table, the drawing boards, and the floor. Ramona was splashed with red and yellow paint. Blue and green ran down Wayne's jeans onto his sneakers. A pool of brown paint dripped off the table onto the floor.

"Now see what you did," said Wayne, after he had pried his sucker out of Ramona's fist.

"See what *you* did," contradicted Beezus. "Picking on my little sister like that!" She picked up the paper towel the sucker had been resting on and began to wipe the spatters off Ramona, who continued to howl.

"Boys and girls!" Miss Robbins raised her voice. "Let's be quiet. When the room is quiet I know you are thinking. Lots of people don't know you have to think while you paint." Then she turned to Wayne. "All right, Wayne, you may get a damp cloth and wipe up the paint."

"I'm sorry, Miss Robbins," said Beezus.

"I want the sucker!" screamed Ramona.

Suddenly Beezus decided she had had enough. This art class was one place where Ramona was not supposed to be. She was supposed to play in the sand pile. Mother had said so. She was not supposed to upset the class and spoil everything with one of her tantrums. Beezus made up her mind she was going to do something about it and right now, too, though she didn't know what.

"Ramona, stop that this instant," Beezus ordered. "Go out and play in the sand pile, where you belong, or I'll . . . I'll . . ." Frantically Beezus tried to think what she could do. Then she had an inspiration. "Or I'll tickle you!" she finished. I guess I do have some imagination, after all, she thought triumphantly.

Instantly Ramona stopped crying. She hugged herself and stared at Beezus. "Don't tickle, Beezus," she begged. "Please don't tickle."

"Then go out and play in the sand pile, like Mother says you're supposed to," said Beezus.

"Don't tickle," shrieked Ramona, as she scrambled down from her stool and ran out the door.

Well! thought Beezus. It worked! It really worked!

Feeling suddenly lighthearted, she tacked a fresh sheet of paper to her drawing board and sat staring at it. Maybe Ramona didn't have so much imagination after all, if she couldn't draw a picture of an imaginary green lizard. Well, if Ramona couldn't paint a picture of Ralph, *she* could. Ramona was not the only one in the family with imagination. So there!

Beezus seized her brush and painted in another sky with bold, free strokes. Then she dipped her brush into green paint and started to outline a lizard on her paper. Let's see, what did a lizard look like? She could not remember. It didn't matter much, anyway—not for an imaginary animal. She had started the lizard with such brave, bold strokes that it took up most of the paper and looked more like a dragon.

Beezus promptly decided the animal was a dragon.

Dragons breathed fire, but she did not have any orange paint, and she was so late in starting this picture that she didn't want to take time to mix any. She dipped her brush into pink paint instead and made flames come out of the dragon's mouth. Only they didn't look like flames. They looked more like the spun-sugar candy Beezus had once eaten at the circus. And a dragon breathing clouds of pink candy was more fun than an ordinary flame-breathing dragon.

Forgetting everyone around her, Beezus made the pink clouds bigger and fluffier. Dragons had pointed things down their backs, so Beezus made a row of spines down the back. They did not look quite right—more like slanting sticks than spines. Lollipop sticks, of course!

At that Beezus laughed to herself. Naturally a dragon that breathed pink spun sugar would have lollipops down its back. Eagerly she dipped her brush into red paint, and put a strawberry lollipop on one of the sticks. She painted a different flavor on each stick, finishing with a grape-flavored lollipop like the one Wayne and Ramona had shared.

Then she held her drawing board at arm's length. She was pleased with her dragon. It was funny and colorful and really imaginary. Beezus wondered what she should do next. Then she remembered that Miss Robbins often said it was important for an artist to know when to stop painting. Maybe she'd spoil her picture if she added anything. No, just one more touch. She dipped her brush in yellow paint and gave the dragon an eye—a lemon-drop eye. There! Her imaginary animal was finished!

By that time it was four-thirty and most of the boys and girls had put away their drawing boards and washed their muffin tins. Several mothers who had come for their children were wandering around the room looking at the paintings.

"Those who have finished, wash your hands clean," said Miss Robbins. "And I mean clean." Then she came across the room to Beezus. "Why, Beezus!" she exclaimed. "This is a picture to be proud of!"

"I didn't know whether a dragon should have lollipops down his back or not, but they were fun to paint," said Beezus.

"Of course he can have lollipops down his back. It's a splendid idea. After all, no one has ever seen a dragon, so no one knows how one should look." Miss Robbins turned to several of the mothers and said, with admiration in her voice, "Here's a girl with real imagination."

Beezus smiled modestly at her toes while the mothers admired her picture.

"We'll tack this in the very center of the wall for next week's classes to see," said Miss Robbins.

"It was fun to paint," confided Beezus, her face flushed with pleasure.

"Of course it was," said Miss Robbins, as she carefully placed the picture in the center of the wall. "Didn't I tell you you worked too hard at painting before?"

Beezus nodded. That was the wonderful thing about it, she thought, as she scrubbed out her muffin tins. Her dragon had been fun, while her flying horse had been work. And she had imagination. Maybe not as much as Ramona, but real imagination just the same. "Here's a girl with real imagination," Miss Robbins had said.

A girl with real imagination, a girl with real imagination, Beezus thought as she left the building and ran across the park to the sand pile. "Come on, Ramona, it's time to go home," she called to her little sister, who was happily sprinkling sand on a sleeping dog. "And let's not forget Ralph!" Good old Ralph!

Amazing Animals of Australia

The continent called Australia is a wonderful place to meet strange animals. Because it is a giant island, many kinds of mammals have developed there apart from the rest of the world. Most all are colorful and interesting.

One of the most primitive mammals in the world is the Duck-billed Platypus. He is about the size of a muskrat and lays eggs at the end of a long burrow in the bank of a stream. Instead of a regular mouth the Platypus has a sort of broad bill. This is perfect for catching worms, water bugs, and beetles. His feet have webs between their strong claws and are fine for swimming and digging.

In Australia hundreds of different mammals carry their babies around in fur-lined pouches. Dozens of these pouched creatures, called marsupials, are no longer than mice and rats.

The most famous of Australia's marsupials belong to the kangaroo family. All of the many different kinds have long hind legs with which they can make tremendous leaps. Some of them spend most of their time among the branches of trees. The largest one may be eight feet long from his nose to the tip of his thick tail, and the smallest is only eighteen inches long. Kangaroos live mostly on the leaves and other soft parts of plants.

Australians call a baby kangaroo a "Joey." His mother carries him around in her pouch wherever she goes until

Duck-billed Platypus, a fine swimmer

he is big enough to take care of himself. Sometimes he hitchhikes a ride even when he is old enough to know better!

Australia has about a dozen kinds of medium-size kangaroos known as Rock Wallabies. These fellows have unusually long tails which help to balance them as they leap from boulder to boulder. They are common in rocky places over most of Australia. The bottoms of their feet have nonskid pads to prevent them from slipping.

Rock Wallabies, like other kangaroos, take it easy during

Mother Kangaroo and her "Joey"

Ring-tailed Rock Wallaby *leaps with ease*

the day. Sometimes they take a sun bath on a ledge. They are most active around sunset, when they really sail through the air, like the one in the photographs.

The furry, big-eared Koala is a very different sort of marsupial. He spends his life in eucalyptus trees, holding on with his very sharp claws. He rarely jumps and most of the time he prefers to climb around slowly. The leaves of the eucalyptus trees are his only food, as far as we know, and their moisture is his only drink.

Koala and baby

The baby Koala stays in his mother's pouch while he is very small. Then he starts coming out more and more often. At this point his mother often holds him in her arms. He also learns to ride piggy-back while he clings to her fur with all four feet.

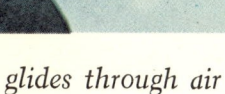

glides through air  *makes a perfect landing!*

Another queer pouched mammal of Australia is the big-eyed, round-faced Spotted Phalanger. He is a relative of our American Opossum, which also sleeps during the day and feeds at night.

One of Australia's smallest marsupials is the Pigmy Possum. His body is only a few inches long, but he eats many kinds of tree blossoms, insects, and wild fruits. His nest of bark and leaves is usually placed in the hollow of a dead tree. And he can hang by his tail from a branch!

The reddish-brown Dingo is Australia's wild dog. He is an appealing puppy, but when full-grown he has a wolf-like face. The Dingo probably came to Australia over a thousand years ago with the ancestors of native tribes. He does his hunting mostly at night.

Spotted Phalanger

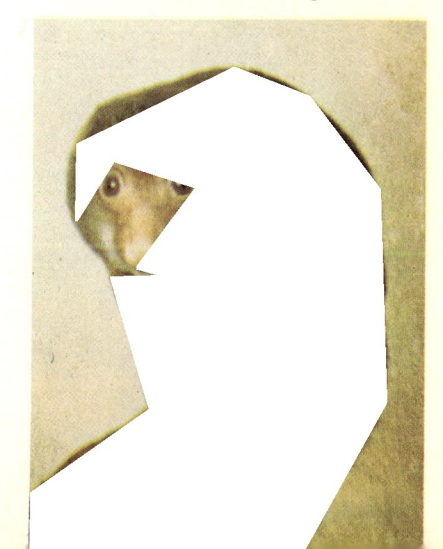

Pigmy Possum is only a few inches long.

For many years naturalists and zoo collectors have gone to study and collect the fascinating animals of Australia. On this large island continent are found some of the most interesting creatures in the world!

Koala in mid-air *Dingo pup*

Printed in the United States of America